The Structure of Knowledge
and the Curriculum

RAND MᶜNALLY CURRICULUM SERIES

EDITED BY J. CECIL PARKER, UNIVERSITY OF CALIFORNIA, BERKELEY

The Structure
and the

ESSAYS BY

JOSEPH J. SCHWAB, UNIVERSITY OF CHICAGO

L. H. LANGE, SAN JOSE STATE COLLEGE

GRAHAM C. WILSON, SAN JOSE STATE COLLEGE

MICHAEL SCRIVEN, INDIANA UNIVERSITY

# of Knowledge
Curriculum

EDITED BY

G. W. FORD, SAN JOSE STATE COLLEGE

LAWRENCE PUGNO, SAN JOSE STATE COLLEGE

Conference on the Structure ...

RAND McNALLY & COMPANY · CHICAGO

RAND MᶜNALLY EDUCATION SERIES

B. OTHANEL SMITH, ADVISORY EDITOR

Broudy and Palmer, *Exemplars of Teaching Method*

Broudy, Smith, and Burnett, *Democracy and Excellence in American Secondary Education*

Farwell and Peters, eds., *Guidance Readings for Counselors*

Foshay, ed., *Rand MᶜNally Handbook of Education*

Haines, *Guiding the Student Teaching Process in Elementary Education*

Kimbrough, *Political Power and Educational Decision-Making*

Lewenstein, *Teaching Social Studies in Junior and Senior High Schools*

Litwack, Holmes, and O'Hern, *Critical Issues in Student Personnel Work*

Norris, Zeran, and Hatch, *The Information Service in Guidance: Occupational, Educational, Social*

Parker, ed., *Rand MᶜNally Curriculum Series*

Ford and Pugno, eds., *The Structure of Knowledge and the Curriculum*

Peters and Farwell, *Guidance: A Developmental Approach*

Peters, Shertzer, and Van Hoose, *Guidance in Elementary Schools*

Rollins and Unruh, *Introduction to Secondary Education*

Smith and Ennis, eds., *Language and Concepts in Education*

Trump and Baynham, *Focus on Change: Guide to Better Schools*

Vassar, ed., *Social History of American Education*, 2 volumes

Wellington and Wellington, *The Underachiever*

Zeran and Riccio, *Organization and Administration of Guidance Services*

Also published by Rand MᶜNally

Gage, ed., *Handbook of Research on Teaching*—A Project of the American Educational Research Association

CONTENTS

·

FOREWORD

•

These papers originally were presented as lectures in the first Curriculum Conference of San Jose State College (California) Division of Education. The Conference explored common curriculum problems of elementary and secondary schools and considered the structure of knowledge in four major disciplines that provide subject matter for the schools curriculum.

This book continues the examination of the nature and structure of knowledge which has been receiving the serious attention of educators in the past few years. It is not the beginning of that examination. The beginning is difficult to determine, but certainly Bruner's *The Process of Education*[1] was most timely and focused attention on the concept of structure as related to learning.

These essays will not complete the examination; indeed, much more will have to be considered, stated, and assessed before the examination can be considered to be beyond the beginning stages. It could well be that the concept "structure of knowledge" is an educational expression *in search of definition*. The following essays will be most helpful in that search.

Other major efforts to define the nature and structure of knowledge as they relate to the general curriculum have preceded this conference. Foshay's proposals, which reflected able and clear thinking about curriculum, were presented to the 1961 conference of the Association for Supervision and Curriculum Development. His proposal that curriculum workers question scholars in the disciplines regarding the structure of their fields, and that in turn such scholars accept seriously the task

---

[1] Jerome S. Bruner, *The Process of Education* (Cambridge: Harvard University Press, 1962).

1

of communicating their answers to teachers and curriculum makers, has been acted upon in this publication and at its related conference.

Another major effort which brought together scholars and educators was the National Education Association Project on Instruction. In discussing the purpose of the disciplines seminar associated with the project, the following statement was made:

> The Seminar was called to facilitate study and effective use of the disciplines by (a) focusing upon those fundamental ideas and methods of inquiry from selected fields of study which should be in the mainstream of the instructional program of the public schools, and (b) exploring frontier thinking and research in the nature of knowledge and ways of knowing.[2]

The reader wishing to keep abreast of developments in this field can ill afford to miss the statements and summaries of the Disciplines Seminar.

One other major contribution to defining the structure of knowledge should be mentioned—the Conference on the Nature of Knowledge held in 1961 at the University of Wisconsin-Milwaukee. The conference report contains several addresses that directly treat the structure of knowledge.[3]

STRUCTURE

Structure is not a difficult concept. It refers to the parts of an object and the ways in which they are interrelated. The structure of a molecule would be its atomic constituents and the ways the atoms are arranged. The structure of a curriculum would be the various subjects and educational activities and their vertical and horizontal arrangement. The educator's reference to the scope and sequence of curriculum illustrates structure as applied to curriculum considerations.

Using the examples of molecular structure and curricular structure, two points concerning structure can be identified.

[2] *The Scholars Look at the Schools: A Report of the Disciplines Seminar* (Washington, D.C.: National Education Association, 1962), pp. 1–2.

[3] William A. Jenkins (ed.), *The Nature of Knowledge* (Milwaukee, Wis.: University of Wisconsin–Milwaukee, University Bookstore, 1962).

Structure of Knowledge

The first is that in all considerations of the structure of an object, assumptions must be made relative to identifying parts. The second is that knowledge of the structure of an object tells one little or nothing about the relation of that object to other objects. Both of these points have major implications for curriculum development.

The first point is concerned with the parts of an object. The chemist generally views the parts of a molecule as being atoms. He does not generally need to concern himself with the structure of the atom. The chemist accepts the unanalyzed atom as the significant part of the structure of the molecule, even though the physicist would consider the atom as a complex object with a wealth of structural features to investigate. Also, the total curriculum of the school is part of a more inclusive structure—perhaps the structure of knowledge—and it in turn is composed of structures generally labeled subjects (themselves amenable to analysis into additional structures).

The second point identifies a major curriculum problem. As was stated, knowledge of the structure of an object provides little information about the relation of that object to other objects. Thorough knowledge of the structure of a particular molecule does not in itself provide knowledge of how that molecule will react with other molecules. The structural knowledge of chemistry is required before that is possible. In curricular terms, this means that knowledge of the structure of history, mathematics, and science does not enable us to organize either knowledge or the curriculum. This is not to say that clarity regarding the structure of mathematics is unimportant, but that to the curriculum builder such clarity is insufficient for his task.

CURRICULUM

These and other considerations suggest that in so far as teachers and curriculum planners are concerned, knowledge of the structure of the major disciplines does not and cannot provide all the answers to designing a curriculum. What then is the value in a thorough and complete examination of the disciplines for the curriculum builder? And how does such an examination fit into the other factors that should be considered in developing

3

curriculum for today's schools? Ralph Tyler touched upon these important questions in his remarks at the end of the conference.

> From the standpoint of the curriculum, the disciplines should be viewed primarily as a resource that can be drawn upon for the education of students. Hence, we want to understand these resources at their best. And we, I think properly, are often fearful that some of the second-hand treatment that we get of these subjects really prostitutes them—does not represent them at their best. Certainly these disciplines at their best are not simply an encyclopedic collection of facts to be memorized but rather they are an active effort to make sense out of some portion of the world or of life.

Thus those concerned with the curriculum of the schools must in some way maintain close contacts with scholars in the disciplines so that the nature and contributions of the disciplines are accurately reflected. But let us be clear. Full knowledge of the disciplines associated with the school subjects is insufficient for defining the curriculum—other factors must be considered. In his comments to the conference, Dr. Tyler suggested what some of these considerations should be.

> We are looking for sources as we plan the curriculum. But after making an inventory of the best of these resources from the disciplines, the curriculum builder then must seek to develop a balanced and effective curriculum plan, and this involves consideration and weighing of several factors.
>
> We want to know what is needed today. What kinds of demands are going to be made of our young people? What sort of equipment will they have to have in order to carry on life in the modern world? What are the opportunities provided by the modern world for the greater fulfillment of youth—for greater service on the one hand and greater enjoyment on the other?
>
> We also need to look carefully at the particular situation of children and youth at the school that concerns us, because there are not only differences within any school but also communities differ in respect to the backgrounds of children, what they have learned previously, what kinds of attitudes they have towards

4

learning. The difference between the conditions of a school in the slum area of one of our large cities and the school in the wealthy suburban community is almost as great as any difference you could find between one country and another country.

Then there is the problem of learning and teaching. The National Science Foundation in updating the scientific and mathematical studies in the schools through use of practicing scientists and scholars, quickly discovered that, in order to get material that was teachable, they needed to involve teachers and pupils. The new projects that are just being started in the social studies have as their initial effort the development of units to be tried out by scholars, scientists, teachers, and children so that they do not recommend material until they have evidence about its potential in an actual teaching situation.

Another factor to be considered in curriculum selection is the worth of the material in contributing to human values. How does it help in developing respect for the dignity and worth of every human being? How far does it promote our belief in the importance of intelligence, initiative, and independence? These values which are basic to our society are basically important to curriculum development and need to be taken into account.

In summary, although many factors—the needs and characteristics of students and society, and the way learning takes place—must be considered in designing the curriculum, if curriculum development is to proceed properly, each school subject, along with its associated discipline(s), should be under constant examination. The disciplines need examination in terms of their structure. The school subjects should be reviewed to determine whether recent findings in the disciplines are, or should be, reflected in the subject. It was the purpose of the Conference on the Structure of Knowledge and the Curriculum to carry out such an examination, and this volume is dedicated to that purpose.

G. W. F.
L. P.

San Jose, California

JOSEPH J. SCHWAB

●

STRUCTURE OF THE DISCIPLINES: MEANINGS AND SIGNIFICANCES

We embark here on an exploration of one of the most difficult of terrains: investigation of the nature, variety, and extent of human knowledge; and the attempt to determine what that nature, variety, and extent have to tell us about teaching and learning. My share of this task is a specialized one and a preliminary one. It is simply to map that terrain. Later papers will explore the land itself.

What is meant by the structure of the disciplines? It means three things, three distinct but related sets of problems. Let us take a foretaste of all three together without discriminating them by name.

It has been widely supposed that there are indubitable grounds for recognizing basically different orders of phenomena, each requiring a different discipline for its investigation because of the differences in the character of the phenomena.

There are many different views based on such a premise. For example, many philosophers have insisted on a fundamental distinction between living phenomena and non-living, thus generating the notion that there are two fundamentally different sciences, the biological and the physio-chemical. These two sciences were supposed to differ in method, in guiding conceptions, in the kind of knowledge produced, and in degree of certainty, differing to precisely the same extent that their subject matters were supposed to differ.

Another such view is generated by a distinction between

man and nature, a distinction in which nature is conceived as bound by inexorable laws while men are in some sense and in some degree free. In this view, two major areas of investigation are again discriminated: on the one hand, science, concerned with the inexorable laws that nature presumably obeys; and on the other hand, a discipline in the neighborhood of ethics and politics, which would investigate the freedom that man has and the ways in which men make their choices.

There is also a view that emphasizes the vast difference between the generality of "natural" phenomena (i.e., their predictability, the tendency of "natural" things to behave or be the same in instance after instance) and the particularity of human events (the essentially unique and non-repeating character of acts notable in the behavior of man). Again, two widely different bodies of investigation and study are generated: science on the one hand and history on the other. Science, in this view, would seek the general laws that characterize the repeating behavior of natural things, while history would seek to determine the precise, unique events that characterized each life, each era, each civilization or culture that it studied. Hence, again, there would be two basically different curriculum components, differing in method, principle, and warrantability.

There have been similar separations of other disciplines, notably mathematics and logic. Mathematics was long ago seen to differ radically from other disciplines, including the sciences, in that its subject matter appeared to have no material existence. The objects of physical or biological enquiry could be seen, touched, smelled, tasted. The objects of mathematics could not. The plane, the line, the point, unity, number, etc. existed in some way which was not material or did not exist at all. This peculiarity of mathematical objects continues to be a puzzle. No one view of the nature of mathematics has been developed which is satisfactory to all concerned, though most moderns are agreed that mathematics differs radically from the other sciences.

Logic has been set apart because of its unique relationship to other disciplines rather than because of something peculiar about its subject matter. To one degree or another, all other disciplines test the reliability of their conclusions by appealing to canons of reasoning and of evidence which are developed in the first place by the discipline of logic. Since logic is responsible for developing these canons, it cannot itself use them to check its own work. Logic thus stands as a sort of "queen of the sciences," dictating their rules but having for itself rules of some other and puzzling sort. Unlike the case of mathematics, this peculiarity of logic is no longer universally recognized. In some quarters, for example, it is held that logic does no more than formulate the methods and the canons of reasoning and of evidence which other sciences have developed, used, and bear witness to by their effectiveness. In this view, logic is not so much the queen of the sciences as their handmaiden.

Let us continue our foretaste of the problems of the structures of the disciplines by noting a peculiarity of the distinctions we have described. The peculiarity is that the differences among phenomena which appear at one period in the history of the disciplines to be radical and self-evident may at a later date disappear or become inconsequential as bases for differentiating disciplines. Take, for example, the differentiation of biology from the physical-chemical sciences. In early times and through the eighteenth century, fundamental differences between the living and the non-living could not be evaded. The living thing was "self-moving"; no other object was. The living thing reproduced itself; the living thing developed, had a personal history which no non-living thing could duplicate. Then, in the middle to late nineteenth century, some of these differences ceased to be notable, others disappeared entirely from human recognition. In this altered climate, the physiologist Claude Bernard pleaded for a study of living things strictly in terms of physics and chemistry. Since then, such an approach to living things has been so fruitful that it is now safe to say that it will be only a brief time before we shall synthesize living molecules in the laboratory. In recent years a still further shift in outlook has taken place: we now hear pleas from some physicists that certain physical phenomena be treated in much the way that living things were investigated *before* Bernard.

A similar shift is visible on a smaller scale in the history of the science of mechanics. Three hundred years ago the behavior of celestial bodies (the planets and the stars) and the behavior of terrestrial bodies in motion (things rolling on the surface of the earth and things thrown or propelled through the air) appeared to be radically different. Terrestrial bodies inevitably came to rest and fell to earth; celestial bodies inevitably continued in their regular motion without stop. Then, with Newton, these differences, though still visible, became entirely unimportant.

In brief, what we see of and in things changes from epoch to epoch. Differences that once appeared to be radical are seen later to be illusory or trivial; then, at another period, some of these differences reappear in a new guise. What can account for such changes in what appears to be objectively perceived? The answer is most easily exemplified in the case of mechanics, where in our own day the once radical difference between terrestrial and celestial bodies continues to be treated as illusory.

Granted that this difference was an illusion, what made the illusion disappear? The answer is this: Newton conceived an idea called universal gravitation. In the light of this idea, it became desirable and possible to examine the motion of the celestial bodies (in Newton's case, the moon) in a new way. Specifically, it became desirable and possible to measure the changing directions and changing velocities of the moon in such a fashion that it could be described as continually falling toward earth, while, at the same time, continually moving in a straight line at an angle to its fall. Thus its continuous orbit of the earth could be understood as the resultant of these two motions. In the same way it became possible to conceive of a terrestrial missile as falling to earth and coming to rest there only because its initial velocity in a straight line was not great enough to carry it straight forward beyond the bend of the earth before its fall brought it into contact with the earth. One could then see that as the initial velocity of a missile became greater and greater, it would not only go farther before it fell to earth, but at some point the increased velocity would be so great that the fall of the missile would be compensated by the falling away of the spherical surface of the earth. Such a missile would then become a satellite of the earth precisely like the moon. In brief, a new conception dictating new studies and a new way to interpret the data exhibited the movement of celestial bodies as nothing more than an extreme case of the motions of familiar terrestrial bodies moving at lower velocities.

In general, two collections of phenomena appear to be vastly different because we have used separate and distinct bodies of conceptions in studying them and discovering knowledge about them. Each such body of conceptions dictates what data we think we should seek, what experiments to perform, and what to make of our data by way of knowledge. If widely different conceptions are used to guide enquiries on two different collections of phenomena, we end inevitably with bodies of knowledge which exhibit few similarities and many differences. It is through the limiting or distorting lenses of these bodies of knowledge that we look at things. Hence, if the lenses distort or limit in different ways, we see things as different. The differences we see disappear if, but only if, a new conception is given birth which permits the study of both collections of phenomena in one set of terms and therefore makes for unity where diversity existed before.

Before we discriminate the problems of the structure of the disciplines, let us take note of a *caveat*. It is this: the integration of previously separate bodies of knowledge by new and unifying conceptions should not blind us to the possibility that some of the differences we recognize among phenomena may be genuine; some differentiation of disciplines may be perennial. There really may be joints in nature, a forearm, then an elbow, and then an upper arm. Science, ethics, and aesthetics may indeed represent three widely variant objects of enquiry. The doctrine of the unity of science, which insists on a unification of all knowledge, is either a dogma or a hope but not a fact. There are no data from which to conclude decisively that eventually all the disciplines will become or should become one.

Now let us step back and identify in this foretaste of knowledge and knowledge-seeking the three major but related sets of problems which define the area called structure of the disciplines.

Recall first our brief review of efforts to discriminate life from non-life, science from history, and so on. These efforts illustrate the first problem of the structure of the disciplines. It is the problem of determining the membership and organization of the disciplines, of identifying the significantly different disciplines, and of locating their relations to one another.

This set of problems is illustrated by the following questions. *Is* mathematical knowledge significantly different from knowledge of physical things? If so, how are the behaviors of mathematical objects related to the behaviors of physical objects? That is, how must we account for the extraordinary usefulness of mathematics to the sciences? Is it because we impose mathematical forms on our observation of physical things, or is it because, in some mysterious way, the objects of the external world behave according to patterns that we discover through mathematical enquiry into our own intellects? Similarly, we might raise questions about practical knowledge and scientific or theoretical knowledge. Are they much the same or truly different? Is practical knowledge merely the application of science? Or does science take hold of ideal objects extrapolated from experience of things while practical knowledge must supply the bridge for return from scientific knowledge of such ideal objects to the actual and practicable? This set of problems may properly be called a problem of the structure of the disciplines, if we keep in mind that by the plural "disciplines" we refer to them collectively rather than distributively, while "structure" is singular and refers to the organization of the disciplines *inter se*.

The significance of this set of problems to education is obvious enough. To identify the disciplines that constitute contemporary knowledge and mastery of the world, is to identify the subject matter of education, the material that constitutes both its resources and its obligations. To locate the relations of these disciplines to one another is to determine what may be joined together for purposes of instruction and what should be held apart; these same relations will also weigh heavily in determining our decisions about the sequence of instruction, for it will tell us what must come before what, or what is most desirably placed first, or second, or third.

The second set of problems of the structure of the disciplines is exemplified by the tremendous role of the concept of universal gravitation in supplying us with a more nearly universal mechanics. A similar role is played by other conceptions in the attainment and formulation of all scientific knowledge. Embedded in the knowledge we have of the workings of the human body lies one or another concept of the nature of an organism, of the character of the parts of such an organism and how they relate to one another. Back of our knowledge of heredity lies a conception of particles behaving as do the terms in the expansion of a binominal to the second or higher powers. Back of our ability to make decisions in playing games lie similar conceptions. Again, the conceptions happen to be mathematical: the expansion of the binominal or a more complex mathematical structure derived by taking the expansion of the binominal to its limit. These mathematical conceptions provide us with a body of probability theory with which we play poker, determine tactics in battle, plan the production and sale of the products of our industries. Similarly, knowledge of human behavior, both individual and social, has arisen only as the men concerned with enquiry in psychology, sociology, and anthropology have developed conceptions that have enabled them to plan their researches.

In general then, enquiry has its origin in a conceptual structure, often mathematical, but not necessarily so. It is this conceptual structure through which we are able to formulate a telling question. It is through the telling question that we know what data to seek and what experiments to perform to get those data. Once the data are in hand, the same conceptual structure tells us how to interpret them, what to make of them by way of knowledge. Finally, the knowledge itself is formulated in the terms provided by the same conception. Thus we formulate and convey some of the knowledge we discover about the body in terms of organs and functions; we formulate and communicate our knowledge of atomic structure in terms of a concept of particles and waves; we formulate some of our knowledge of human personality in terms of psychic organs and their functions and other portions of it in terms of interpersonal relations.

In each science and in many arts such conceptual structures prevail. The second problem of the structure of the disciplines is to identify these structures and understand the powers and limits of the enquiries that take place under their guidance. Let us call this set of problems the problem of the *substantive* structures of each discipline.

Again, the significance of this problem of the structure of the disciplines to education is obvious enough—or at least one part of it is. For to know what structures underlie a given body of knowledge is to know what problems we shall face in imparting this knowledge. Perhaps the conceptual structure is no more complex than that involved in the discrimination of two classes of things by a single criterion, such as color or shape. In that case, we may suppose that little difficulty would be encountered in teaching this body of knowledge even to the very young. Perhaps the conceptual structure is more complex but so firmly embedded in common-sense knowledge of things that the child at some early, given age will already have encountered it and become familiar with it. In that case, we should, again, have little difficulty in imparting our knowledge, provided that we impart it at the right time in the development of the child in our culture. However, suppose the conceptual structure is both complex and largely unused in common-sense knowledge? This would be the case at the moment for the physical conception of a wave-like particle. In such a case, to locate and identify the conception is to locate and identify a difficult problem of instruction requiring much experiment and study.

A second curricular significance of the problem of the substantive structures of each discipline is less obvious. It concerns a peculiar consequence of the role of conceptual structures on our knowledge, a consequence little noted until recently. The dependence of knowledge on a conceptual structure means that any body of knowledge is likely to be of only temporary significance. For the knowledge which develops from the use of a given concept usually discloses new complexities of the subject matter which call forth new concepts. These new concepts in turn give rise to new bodies of enquiry and, therefore, to new and more complete bodies of knowledge stated in new terms. The significance of this ephemeral character of knowledge to education consists in the fact that it exhibits the desirability if not the necessity for so teaching what we teach that students understand that the knowledge we possess is not mere literal, factual truth but a kind of knowledge which is true in a more complex sense. This in turn means that we must clarify for students the role of concepts in making knowledge possible (and limiting its validity) and impart to them some idea of the particular concepts that underlie present knowledge of each subject matter, together with the reasons for the appropriateness of these concepts and some hint of their limitations.[1]

The third problem of the structure of the disciplines we shall call the problem of the *syntactical* structure of the disciplines. This problem is hidden in the fact that if different sciences pursue knowledge of their respective subject matters by means of different conceptual frames, it is very likely that there will be major differences between one discipline and another in the way and in the extent to which it can verify its knowledge. There is, then, the problem of determining for each discipline what it does by way of discovery and proof, what criteria it uses for measuring the quality of its data, how strictly it can apply canons of evidence, and in general, of determining the route or pathway by which the discipline moves from its raw data through a longer or shorter process of interpretation to its conclusion.

Again, certain obvious consequences to education accrue from such a study. For, unless we intend to treat all knowledge as literal, true dogma, and thereby treat students as mere passive, obedient servants of our current culture, we want our students to know, concerning each body of knowledge learned, how sound, how dependable it is.

In summary then, three different sets of problems constitute the general problem of the structure of the disciplines. First there is the problem of the organization of the disciplines: how many there are; what they are; and how they relate to one another. Second, there is the problem of the substantive conceptual structures used by each discipline. Third, there is the problem of the syntax of each discipline: what its canons of evidence and proof are and how well they can be applied. Let us turn now to a brief investigation of each of these problems.

---

[1] See Joseph J. Schwab, "Enquiry, the Science Teacher, and the Educator," *School Review*, LXVIII (Summer 1960), for an elaboration of this point.

Structure of the Disciplines: Meanings and Significances

THE PROBLEM OF THE ORGANIZATION OF THE DISCIPLINES

With the problem of the organization of the disciplines we must face at once one of the inevitable complexities of this terrain, the fact that it does not and cannot supply a single, authoritative answer to the question of what disciplines there are, how many there are, and how they are related to one another. The reason for this complexity is fairly obvious. The problem of organization is a problem of classification primarily. If we classify any group of complex things, we are faced with a wide choice of bases of classification. (Even with postage stamps, we could classify by country of origin, by color, by shape or size, or by some combination of two or more of these.) Disciplines are very complex, hence the diversity and variety of available modes of classification are great. Consequently, depending on what one emphasizes about the disciplines, one or another or still a third or a fifth or a tenth classification of them is generated.

Four bases of classification of disciplines have always demanded attention: (1) their subject matter, what they aim to investigate, or work upon; (2) their practitioners, what competences and habits are required to carry on their work; (3) their methods (syntax), and modes of enquiry by which the enquirer brings himself to bear on the subject matter; (4) their ends, the kinds of knowledge or other outcomes at which they aim. Let us, then, examine a few organizations of the disciplines which use one or more of these, choosing them for the light they may throw on current curriculum problems.

The basic organization of the sciences proposed by Aristotle is worth taking a brief look at nowadays because we have tended to forget what it emphasizes. In this organization, Aristotle made most use of the end or aim of the disciplines together with the character of the materials they work on, the subject matter. Using these two as bases of classification, Aristotle distinguished three major groups of disciplines, the names of which have survived even in our current commonsense knowledge of the disciplines—though the significance assigned them has altered or been lost. The three basic divisions are the *Theoretical,* the *Practical,* and the *Productive.*

Joseph J. Schwab

The theoretical disciplines are those whose aim is to know. For Aristotle, "to know" meant to know indubitably. Therefore, the theoretical disciplines included only those whose subject matters exhibited such inexorable regularity that they could be considered proper objects of "knowing" enquiry. Aristotle thought there were three such "knowing" or theoretical disciplines: physics, mathematics, and metaphysics. Today, though we would be very doubtful about the possibility of indubitable knowledge, we would, nevertheless, recognize a group of "theoretical" disciplines whose aim was to know and whose subject matters were such that the knowledge these disciplines sought was as nearly stable as knowledge can be. We would include the physical and biological sciences in this group. We would include substantial portions of the social sciences. We would exclude metaphysics as doubtful indeed. We would exclude mathematics, not because it is doubtful, but because we would consider it very special.

The practical disciplines, for Aristotle, included those concerned with choice, decision, and action based on deliberate decision. Precisely because its aim was to do, and therefore to alter the course of things, its subject matter had to have the property that was exactly opposite to the property required for the theoretical sciences. The subject matters of the practical sciences by necessity, must be not inexorable in their behavior, but capable of alteration, not fixed and stable but changeable.

It is exceedingly important, if we are to appreciate the bearing of this Aristotelian classification on modern problems, that we realize that "deliberate action" meant for Aristotle actions undertaken for their *own sakes* and not actions undertaken merely as the necessary preliminaries to some other end. Such actions, undertaken for their own sakes, constitute, then, what we mean by "a good life." They are the activities that stem from and express the best of which each man is capable. The practical sciences were (and are) therefore, ethics and politics. For us in modern times, ethics and politics would include not only each individual effort to lead and examine a deliberate life and the governing and policymaking in high places, but also the difficult and terrifying business of being parents, of being teachers *deliberately* and not as automatons, and the responsible work of administration and policymaking at all levels, together with those parts of the social sciences which contribute to such activities. I need not add that of all the things the schools might do, they do least of this. A few nursery schools, a very few teachers at the elementary level, and some few men and women at the college level give thought and time and energy toward evoking in their students the competencies and habits that lead to the making of good choices and good decisions and help the person to act in ways commensurate with his decisions. But by and large, the time, the energy, and the resources of our public schools ignore the very existence of practical disciplines in the Aristotelian sense.

The productive disciplines in the Aristotelian scheme are what the work "productive" suggests. They are the disciplines devoted to *making:* the fine arts, the applied arts, engineering. In connection with the significance of the Aristotelian productive disciplines for modern curriculum problems, let us note a principal characteristic of the entire Aristotelian organization: it emphasizes the sharp differences among the three groups of disciplines. The theoretical disciplines, devoted to knowing, concern themselves with those aspects of things which are fixed, stable, enduring. Hence, the theoretical disciplines are concerned with precisely these aspects of things which we cannot alter by making or make use of by doing. The productive disciplines are concerned with what is malleable, capable of being changed. The practical disciplines are concerned with another sort of malleability of human character, its ability to deliberate on its future and (within limits) to do as it sees fit.

We, on the other hand, have tended to fall into the habit of treating all disciplines proper to the schools as if they were theoretical. We manage to maintain this preoccupation in the case of the practical disciplines by ignoring them. In the case of the productive disciplines, we ignore them in some cases and in others resort to the trick of treating them as if they were theoretical. Music appreciation is taught as if its purpose were to recognize obvious themes of symphonies or concertos and proudly announce the opus number and the composer's name. Performing music is taught as if the aim were merely to follow the notes and obey the teacher's instructions about the score.

Literature is taught as if dramas and novels were windows looking out on life, or worse, as if, as in the case of music appreciation, the object of the game were to know choice tidbits about the character, the life, or the times of the author. Art is taught, like literature, as if its aim were to provide a true, a faithful photograph of life. Happily, the exceptions to these strictures are increasing. Music appreciation is more and more being taught as a mastery of those arts by which the ear and the mind creatively take in the form and content of music. Performing music is more and more being taught in such a way that the students learn the grounds by which to discover and select from alternative interpretations of the score. Poetry, literature, and drama are more and more the objects of the kind of scrutiny which permits their appreciation as works of art rather than as sources of vicarious experience. More and more teachers of art permit their students the freedom for creation which society has long since accorded the professional artist. Nevertheless, the theoretizing of the productive disciplines is still prevalent enough to render this warning relevant.

Let us turn to another organization of the sciences, notable in that one version of it is reborn with every undergraduate generation. This is Auguste Comte's positive hierarchy of the sciences. This scheme is based on the view that subject matter, and only subject matter, should provide the basis for classification. It takes the further view that subject matters should be ordered in terms of *their* subject matters; that is, Comte maintains that orders of phenomena can be discerned, each order consisting of members of the next lower order organized into more complex structures. Using this Chinese box conception of the world, Comte locates physical things as the simplest of all orders (presumably something like our modern fundamental particles). Chemicals come next, as consisting of physicals organized in a new way. Then come biologicals as still higher organizations of chemicals. Finally, at the top, come socials as organizations of biologicals. Thus the Comtian hierarchy of the sciences runs: physics, chemistry, biology, the social sciences. Then Comte adds one last factor. At the bottom of the entire structure he places another "science"—mathematics, mathematics conceived as a kind of natural logic governing the study of all the sciences above it.

Perhaps because of its simplicity and its tendency to be reborn in every generation, this particular organization of the disciplines has been one of the most tyrannical and unexamined curriculum principles in our time. It has dictated, I suspect, at least thirty-five per cent of all the sequences and orders of study of the sciences at the high school and college level in the country. The biologist tries to make his task easier by insisting that chemistry precede his subject field. In turn, the chemist demands that physics precede his. The physicist demands that mathematics precede physics. And each appeals to the Comtian hierarchy as the principal reason for his demand.

There is some justice in this view but there is injustice too. For it is quite possible to read the Comtian hierarchy the other way around. The inverted reading can, indeed, be done without departing from Comte's own principles, as Comte himself well knew. The principle in question requires that each science in the hierarchy shall be well developed before the one above it can be developed. Thus an adequate sociology must wait upon a thoroughly adequate biology; biology, in turn, cannot become complete until chemistry is complete, and so on. This *seems* to suggest that physics ought to be developed by a study simply of physical things, postponing chemistry until the study of physicals is complete; in the same way chemistry would be developed by a study of chemicals, postponing biology until the chemistry is complete. However, if we look closely at the basic Comtian principles, we realize that a complete, positive knowledge of the constituents and the organization of chemicals can be developed only if we have sought out and identified all the behaviors of which chemicals are capable. At this point arises the startling corollary that leads to an inverted reading of the Comtian hierarchy. For, clearly, if biologicals are organizations of chemicals, biologicals constitute the place in which some large array of chemical potentialities becomes real and can be seen. It follows, then, that a study of biologicals must precede any completion of chemistry; a study of socials must, in the same way, precede complete knowledge of biologicals, and so on.

The developments of science since the days of Comte most certainly bear out this reading of his hierarchy. Organic chemistry has developed only as we have studied the complex chemistry of the living organism. The behavior of the human individual has become better understood as we have studied human culture and society. The development by physicists of adequate theories of atomic structure rests upon knowledge of chemicals. Thus we see that it is just as plausible to read the Comtian hierarchy downward from sociology through biology, chemistry, and physics to mathematics, as it is to read it upward from mathematics to physics, to chemistry, to biology, and finally to social science.

We cannot, then, rest our arguments for mathematics as prerequisite to physics, physics prerequisite to chemistry, and so on, on the assumption that the upward reading of the Comtian hierarchy constitutes an unequivocal curriculum principle. Rather, we might well argue that bits and portions of each of these alleged prerequisites should be taught as the need arises during the study of the higher sciences. For example, physics might well be taught by examining the obvious behaviors of physical things up to the point where it becomes clear to student and teacher alike that further progress in the physics requires mastery of certain mathematical conceptions or operations. At this point, the class would turn to the mastery of the mathematics required by the physics under study. In the same way, the complex study of the microchemistry of the living cell would not be taught as a prerequisite to study of the organism and its larger parts and functions; rather, the visible behaviors of the organism, of its organ systems and gross organs might well come first, with the biochemical materials so placed as to be meaningful to the students as the physio-chemical basis for the behaviors already known.

The curriculum sequence of prerequisites based on the upward reading of the Comtian hierarchy (i.e., mathematics to physics to chemistry, etc.) is often referred to as the "logical order" of instruction. The fact that the Comtian hierarchy can be read plausibly in either direction requires us to realize, however, that the phrase "logical order" applied only to one of them is a special pleading. Either order is "logical." The upward order from mathematics to the social sciences we might well call the dogmatic order, i.e., the order that runs from the current explanation to that which is explained. The downward order from, say, biology to chemistry, we might call the order of enquiry, i.e., the order that runs from a display of phenomena calling for explanation to the explanation the science has developed. A curriculum choice between the order of enquiry and the dogmatic order cannot be made on subject-matter criteria alone. Rather, we must look to the capacities of our students, to knowledge of ways in which learning takes place, and to our objectives, what we hope our students will achieve, in order to make our decision.

THE PROBLEM OF THE SYNTAX OF THE DISCIPLINES

If all disciplines sought only to know and if the knowledge they sought were merely the simple facts, the syntax of the disciplines would be no problem. As we have seen, the disciplines are not this simple. Many are not, in the Aristotelian sense, theoretical at all: they seek ends that are not knowledge but something else—making, the appreciation of what is made, the arts and habits of deliberation, choice, and action. Those that are theoretical seek knowledge of different kinds (commensurate to their subject matters), hence use different methods and different canons of evidence and warrantability. For example, science seeks very general or even universal knowledge, while much history seeks the most detailed and particular knowledge. Each of these objects of enquiry poses problems peculiar to itself. Hence knowledge of each of them is sought in different ways. Even within the sciences there is much variability. Biologists find it necessary or desirable to seek knowledge in bits and pieces while physicists, at the other extreme, work hard to develop broad, comprehensive theories which embrace vast ranges of subject matter. The evidence that justifies the acceptance of an isolated bit of knowledge and the evidence that justifies the acceptance of a broad, comprehensive theory are of different sorts. There is a problem, therefore, of determining for each discipline or for small groups of disciplines what pathway of enquiry they use, what they mean by verified knowledge and how they go about this verification.

Joseph J. Schwab

To illustrate this diversity, let us take three "things" that are asserted to exist and to have certain defining properties and behaviors. Let us take, first, an automobile, second, an electron, third, a neutrino. Let the three statements read as follows:

The automobile in front of the house is black.

The electron is a particle with a small mass and a negative electrical charge.

The neutrino is a particle with neither charge nor rest mass.

All three statements, let us suppose, are "true." That they are "true" in different senses becomes plain when we consider the following points. We say that the car in front of the house is black and say it with confidence on two bases. First, we look at the car and its neighborhood and report what we see. Second, we invite a colleague to look at the car and its neighborhood; we repeat the statement that reports what we saw; our colleague nods agreement. This, then, is a very simple syntax of discovery, requiring only a naive, private experience of the objects we propose to make statements about plus a transaction between ourself, another enquirer, and the same objects.

By contrast, the syntax that leads us to assert that the electron is a particle with a small mass and a negative electrical charge is far more complex. The statement most certainly does not rest on the fact that I have looked at an electron and that my colleague has also looked and nodded agreement. It cannot arise from such a syntax because the electron is not visible. It rests, rather, on a syntax that involves looking at quite different things, seeking agreement about them, and then adding two further steps. We note certain phenomena; others note the same; then we seek an *explanation* for what we have seen. For explanation we conceive the existence of a minute particle. To it, we assign precisely the mass and precisely the magnitude and kind of charge which would permit this particle—if it existed—to give rise to the phenomena we have observed. The two additional steps are hidden in the additional process of seeking explanation. First, we conceive of something that would account for the phenomena we are concerned about. However, we are not satisfied to use just any conception that will account for it. Rather, we demand that the conception fulfill a second condition: that it fit in with, be coherent with, the rest of the body of knowledge that constitutes our science. In the case of our electron we meet this condition by choosing a particular mass and a particular charge as its important properties. The choice of a particular mass ties our electron to the entire body of physical knowledge called gravitational dynamics. The assignment of a certain electrical charge ties our particle to our knowledge of electricity and its dynamical laws.

The assertion about the neutrino rests on still a third kind of syntactical structure. For not only are neutrinos invisible by definition but they have been assigned a *lack* of such properties as charge and rest mass which characterize the electron. The assigned lack of such properties means that in the ordinary course of events the behavior of neutrinos would have no detectable consequences, would give rise to no phenomena such as we observed and accounted for by positing the existence of the electron. Instead, the ground for positing the existence of the neutrino was roughly as follows: certain effects were found in a phenomenon called beta decay which appeared to be exceptions to certain of the so-called conservation laws, laws that formed part of the very foundation of the body of physical knowledge. One way to account for these beta decay phenomena would be to treat them as "disproofs" of these conservation laws. Another way would have been to treat the decay phenomena as exceptions to the conservation laws and then to dream up an ad hoc explanation for the exception. Physicists preferred, however (for reasons I shall not go into now), to keep the conservation laws intact and universal, and the only conceived alternative enabling them to retain these laws was to suppose the existence of a well-nigh undetectable particle that carried off the quantities whose disappearance would otherwise have called the conservation laws into question.

We have here, then, three different senses in which statements are said to be "true" or warranted, differences of sense not revealed by the statements themselves. The statements are all of the same form—the automobile is black, the neutrino is such and such, the electron is something else. Only the context, the structure of problem, evidence, inference, and interpretation which constitutes the syntax of discovery behind each statement, would reveal to us the different senses in which each is true.

The significance of this variety of modes of enquiry, of patterns of discovery and verification, lies in this: most statements of most disciplines are like the single words of a sentence. They take their most telling meanings, not from their dictionary sense, not from their sense in isolation, but from their context, their place in the syntax. The meaning of $F = MA$ or of free fall, of electron or neutrino, is understood properly only in the context of the enquiry that produced them.

This need for context of enquiry wherewith to make teaching and learning clear has been almost universally overlooked because of a singular failure in the subject-matter preparation of teachers. They have been permitted to assume, or, indeed, have been flatly told, that "induction" or "scientific method" stands for something simple, single, and well defined. Quite the contrary is true: "induction" is not the name for some single, definite process but merely an honorific word attached by various philosophers to whatever mode of enquiry they favor. To a few philosophers, "induction" means the process of simple enumeration of a large number of instances of something or other by which we try to discern what is common among them. In this view, the outcome of "induction" is "generalization." To other philosophers, "induction" means the analysis of phenomena into unit events and the attempt to find out which events invariably precede which others. To still others, "induction" means the attempt to conceive ideas, however remote they may be from the possibility of direct verification, which will "explain," "account for," "embrace," the largest possible variety of phenomena with the greatest economy.

THE PROBLEM OF THE SUBSTANTIVE STRUCTURES OF THE DISCIPLINES

Let us first redevelop the idea of substantive structures and their role in enquiry as sketched in our introduction.

The fact that we propose to investigate a given subject is to admit that we are, in large part, ignorant of it. We may have some superficial knowledge: we may have dealt with the subject matter as part of our round of practical problems; but the very fact that we propose to investigate the subject means that we mistrust our knowledge or consider it entirely inadequate. Thus, enquiry begins in virtual ignorance. Ignorance however, cannot originate an enquiry. Subjects complex enough to demand enquiry are subjects that confound us by the great variety of characteristics, qualities, behaviors, and interactions they present to our view. This richness paralyzes enquiry, for it is far too much to handle all at once and, in our ignorance, we have no way of discerning the greater from the lesser fact; we cannot discriminate the facts that are most "telling" about our subject matter from those that are trivial. In short, if data are to be collected, we must have some sort of guide to relevance and irrelevance, importance and unimportance.

This role of guide to the enquiry is played by a conception borrowed or invented by the enquirer. These conceptions constitute the substantive structures of a discipline.

Let us take, as an example of a primitive beginning of enquiry, the situation that prevailed in the study of animal behavior some sixty years ago. Our knowledge of the behavior of small aquatic animals at that time was no greater than might have been possessed by an alert, small boy who had watched the darting of fish, the play of tadpoles, and the movements of insect larvae in the ponds and streams of his farm. What, then, should we investigate about these dartings, movements, and plays? Should we ask what needs they serve? Perhaps. Yet we do not even know that needs are involved. Shall we ask what purposes the animals have in mind? We do not know whether they have purposes or not. Shall we then try to discover the patterns of these motions, the order in which they occur? The trouble with this is that when a vast number of movements are involved, we must suppose, by analogy to ourselves, that they do not all belong together. Hence the over-all order of them would be meaningless. Yet we cannot discern each coherent sub-group of motions because we do not yet know either the beginnings ("wants," "needs," "stimuli") or their terminations ("goals," "needs satisfied," "terminal response").

This frustration of enquiry was resolved by appealing to the then popular view that all things, including living things, were no more than simple machines, the pattern of which was the simple one known to nineteenth-century physics. This idea of a simple machine was applied to the study of behavior by supposing that every movement through space of an animal was a response to some single, specific, stimulating factor in the environment. It was further supposed that each such stimulated response could be one of only two possible kinds—a movement toward the stimulus or a movement away from it. Such a movement was dubbed a "tropism," "taxis"; movements toward the stimulus being called positive, those away from the stimulus, negative.

This naive and now obsolete conception removed the frustration of enquiry by giving us questions to ask. We were to determine for each organism what stimuli it responded to and whether it responded in the positive or negative sense. These identified questions in turn determined the pattern of experiment. We were to place our aquatic organism in a tank of water, make sure that all physical stimuli but one were uniform throughout the tank, let one stimulus, light, for example, be of high intensity at one end of the tank and low intensity at the other, and then note, as our important datum, which way the animal went. Then our knowledge of animal behavior was to be summed up in a catalogue of negative and positive tropisms characteristic of each species investigated.

Similar naive conceptions enabled us to begin enquiry in other complex fields. Chemistry was able to make great advances in the study of the array of substances of the world by imposing on them the notion of "element." By "element" was meant a substance of ultimate simplicity, a substance made only of itself and incapable of being changed into another such simple substance. This conception dictated the questions to be asked of matter by chemists and the patterns of experiment. The fundamental question was: into what simpler substance can this substance be decomposed? Hence the patterns of experiment were analysis and synthesis. Similar "elements" were devised to guide our earliest enquiries into human personality. We conceived of each human person as consisting of a greater or lesser quantity of each of a number of "traits." Like the chemical elements, each such "trait" (such as courage, imagination, logical reasoning, assiduity) was supposed to be simple (made of no further sub-traits) and independent of all other traits.

The substantive principles chosen to guide enquiry are controlled by two opposing criteria. One of these I shall call reliability. Reliability requires that the guiding principle be free of vagueness and ambiguity, that the referents of its terms have unequivocal location and limit, and that the measurements or manipulations of these referents can be made precisely and can be repeated with uniform results. The substantive structures cited as examples above meet this criterion as well as could be expected.

They do not, however, satisfactorily fulfill the second criterion, which I shall call validity. Note the failure in each case which illustrates the lack of adequate validity. Animal behavior is reduced to a catalogue of independent responses to independently acting stimuli. Yet our knowledge of ourselves and of higher animals makes it highly unlikely that any animal's behavior will be a repertory of separate and independent responses to stimuli. It is much more likely (we suspect) that previous responses modify later ones and that the response to two stimuli presented simultaneously will *not* be the algebraic sum of the responses to each when presented separately. The idea of simple and independent traits, which enabled us to make a start on a study of human personality, is similarly questionable. It is entirely likely that traits are not independent at all but, rather, affect one another. Further, traits may not be fixed quantities but products of experience, changing as our experience grows and changes. Indeed, it may be that a much richer and more complete understanding of human personality could be achieved by doing away entirely with a notion of traits in any form. The notion of chemical element and compound in its most primitive form we may also suspect to be highly incomplete. It supposes that the properties of a compound arise simply by juxtaposition or union of two or more elements. Yet our experience in art, architecture, and engineering tells us that it is not only the constituents of a compound which confer properties on the compound but the organization of these constituents as well.

In short, the criterion of validity asks that the data we use be not only reliable but representative. It asks that the substantive structure that points to these data as the appropriate data of enquiry reflect as much as possible of the richness and complexity of the subject matter to which it is applied.

The existence of these two criteria is important to us because they lead to two characteristics of knowledge which, in turn, have important implications for curriculum. In the first place, the play of these two criteria confer on scientific knowledge a distinctly revisionary character. In the second place, in some sciences the same interplay leads to the concurrent development of a number of bodies of knowledge of the same subject matter.

The revisionary character of scientific knowledge accrues from the continuing assessment and modification of substantive structures. As investigations proceed under the guidance of an early, naive structure, we begin to detect inconsistencies in our data and disparities between our conclusions and the behavior of our subject. These inconsistencies and disparities help us identify the invalidities in our conception. Meanwhile, the naive structure has enabled us nevertheless to gain some knowledge of our subject and to sharpen our techniques for study. Our new knowledge of the subject, our improved techniques, and our sharpened awareness of inadequacies in our substantive structures enable us to conceive new structures more complex than the old, more adequate to the richness of the subject matter. With the advent of a new structure, the knowledge contained in the older conceptions, though "right" enough in its own terms, is rendered obsolete and replaced by a new formulation which puts old facts and new ones together in more revealing ways.

While different substantive structures tend to succeed one another in physics, chemistry, and biology, other disciplines are characterized by the concurrent utilization of several sets of structures. In the recent study of human personality, for example, two bodies of knowledge competed in the market place at the same time. One body of knowledge had been developed by conceiving personality, after the analogy of the body, as consisting of psychic organs. The other body of knowledge had been developed by conceiving of personalities as arising from the need of persons for one another, as developing, for better or for worse, out of the experience of self and of others. Personality, this body of knowledge held, is best described in terms of the various relations the self can establish with others.

Such a pluralism of substantive structures and of bodies of knowledge is characteristic of the social sciences generally and of many humane studies. There is more than one body of economic knowledge; different anthropologists and different sociologists tackle their problems in different terms and in different ways; different critics use widely different conceptions of the art object in the analysis and evaluation of drama, poetry, music, and painting.

The curricular significances of the revisionary character of knowledge and the plural character of knowledge are too numerous to develop fully here. Let us be satisfied with three.

In the first place, both characteristics point to the danger of a purely dogmatic, inculcative curriculum. If we dogmatically select one of several bodies of theory in a given field and dogmatically teach this as the truth about its subject matter, we shall create division and failure of communication among our citizens. Students of different school systems in different regions who are dogmatically taught different histories of crucial moments in our nation's development are an obvious case in point. It is no less divisive, however, if our future citizens are barred from sharing enjoyment of literature and the arts by having been the victims of different dogmas, or barred from understanding each other by having been inculcated with different dogmatic views of the roots of human action or the origins of culture and civilization. The alternative is to avoid indoctrination. We may, if we like, choose but one of several pluralities of bodies of knowledge. But if we do, let it be taught in such a way that the student learns what substantive structures gave rise to the chosen body of knowledge, what the strengths and limitations of these structures are, and what some of the alternative structures are which give rise to alternative bodies of knowledge.

The revisionary character of knowledge assumes curriculum significance because revisions now take place so rapidly that they will probably occur not once but several times in the lives of our students. If they have been taught their physics, chemistry, or biology dogmatically, their discovery that revision has occurred can lead only to bewilderment and disaffection. Again, the alternative is the teaching of scientific knowledge in the light of the enquiry that produced it. If students discover how one body of knowledge succeeds another, if they are aware of the substantive structures that underlie our current knowledge, if they are given a little freedom to speculate on the possible changes in structures which the future may bring, they will not only be prepared to meet future revisions with intelligence but will better understand the knowledge they are currently being taught.

Joseph J. Schwab

•

THE STRUCTURE OF THE
NATURAL SCIENCES

I shall treat three topics: first, the short-term syntax of the sciences, or, to give it another name, the syntax of stable enquiry; second, the long-term syntax of the sciences, or, alternatively, the syntax of fluid enquiry. I shall then turn to a sketch of the substantive structures of science.

THE SYNTAX OF STABLE ENQUIRY

Let us begin by examining the description of science which has its origin in John Dewey's *How We Think*. This starting point is almost mandatory, for the Deweyan formulation, which describes science as taking place in a sequence of steps, has appeared and reappeared in so many textbook prefaces that it has taken on an official character.

Let us begin our analysis of the useful but misleading details of this formulation with an instance of the sort of enquiry the step-wise description attempts to embody.

Imagine a scientist in the early days of modern biology who noted that most living cells contained small, dark-staining bodies called nuclei near the middle. The scientist wondered what role these dark-staining nuclei played in the economy of the cell. Because of their near universality among cells, he suspected that they played an indispensable role and decided to test this possibility. He did so by means of an experiment intended to provide him with some cells (or, rather, cell fragments) that contained no nucleus as well as with cell fragments that did possess a nucleus. The experiment consisted simply of shaking a number of cells in an appropriate solution. By this means, the experimenter obtained the materials he desired. Let us suppose that he obtained 100 non-nucleated fragments and 100 nucleated fragments of cells. He then proceeded to note the fate of each of these fragments. He found, let us say, that 85 of the non-nucleated fragments died within 24 hours; 10 more of these non-nucleated fragments died in 36 hours, and the remainder in about 48 hours. Meanwhile, he found that 21 of the fragments with nuclei died within 24 hours; a few more died in the ensuing two days, but 65 survived for 13 days. At the end of 30 days a few of these nucleated fragments still lived. On the basis of these results, the scientist asserted that the nucleus was necessary to the life of any cell that has one.

The traditional textbook formulation of scientific method sees in this procedure five distinct steps. The first step is the noting of relevant data. In our example, this corresponds, presumably, to the scientist noting that most cells have nuclei. The second step is the forming of a hypothesis. This would correspond to our biologist supposing that the nucleus is indispensable to the life of the cell. The third step is a plan for test of the hypothesis—the intention to obtain and compare fragments with nuclei and fragments without. Step Four is said to be the execution of the plan (the shaking), and Step Five the drawing of the conclusion from the data so obtained.

One of the most misleading aspects of this description of scientific syntax is contained in the description of the last step as the drawing of a *conclusion*. "Conclusion," as you know, conveys two meanings. It suggests, first, that something has been brought to a close. Second, because it is a logical term, referring to a statement derived correctly from presumably true premises, it suggests that the statement it refers to is true. Therefore, to call the last step of a bit of scientific enquiry the drawing of a conclusion is to suggest that the scientist (a) terminates an enterprise and (b) that he has the truth.

Neither of these characteristics holds good for the case in point nor for most scientific enquiries. This becomes clear if we contrast the formulation of the conclusion (that "the nucleus is necessary to the life of any cell that has one") with the data on which the statement is based. Note, first, that the statement derives, not from a study of all cells or all kinds of cells that possess nuclei, but only a few cells of one kind. Notice, too, that even these limited data did not present a clear picture of non-nucleated cell fragments that died instantly or of nucleated fragments that persisted indefinitely. Quite the contrary, the data were "messy." Some nucleated fragments died as soon as non-nucleated ones, and some non-nucleated fragments survived for many hours.

In no sense, then, ought we to consider the scientist's "conclusion" as conclusive. If there is soundness to his assertion, it derives from something more than the data obtained from this one experiment. It rests not only on the data from this experiment but on numerous other items selected from the body of biological knowledge and taken as true (assumed). It is based on knowledge of the similarity of different kinds of cells, a knowledge that permits generalizing to most cells from an experiment performed on one kind only. It is based on the knowledge that any cell, even under the best of conditions, may die from a number of causes. It rests on experience which suggests that the rough handling involved in the experiment may have contributed to the mortality of the nucleated fragments. It rests even on the decision to ignore the difference between cell *fragments* and whole cells.

Some of these bits of assumed biological knowledge are based on data as "messy" as those underlying the present experiment. Further, these bits of knowledge are *selected* bits. We can expect, then, that later enquiries may reverse or modify some of these basic bits. Another enquirer may make a different selection from the body of scientific knowledge and thus come to a different "conclusion" from that reached by our enquirer, even though he used our enquirer's data. In brief, the typical, isolated scientific enquiry yields neither a terminus to research on the problem nor an unequivocal, logically proved conclusion. Rather, it is a temporary plateau, a momentary equilibrium, which permits the experimenter to go on to other matters, other problems, and other enquiries which will bring him back to his original problem with a new insight or a new method or new data and therefore a revision of his understanding.

Joseph J. Schwab

Let us, therefore, describe the last step of a short-term enquiry, not as the drawing of a conclusion, but as an *interpretation of data*. This is no mere polite shift of language, for to say "interpretation of data" is to convey a notion of the tremendous flexibility permitted to the scientist in his treatment of data and to rule out the misleading suggestion that each such short-term enquiry leads to a definitive end.

We are led to an even more far-reaching change of view if we take note of the fundamental illogic involved in the notion that an experiment of the kind we have described could be asserted to be a "proof" of a hypothesis. The basic logical pattern involved is that of a hypothetical syllogism. In its purely logical form, this pattern is as follows:

If A (our hypothesis) be true

Then, B (a certain outcome, a definite state of affairs accessible to observation) should follow;

If not A, not B.

In practice, it is often easy to fulfill the first half of this logical form. We are often able to say that if our hypothesis (A) be the case, then certain phenomena, consequences of the actual existence of A, should follow. In almost no case, however, can we fulfill the second half of this logical form. We are almost never in a position to say that *only* our hypothesized condition can give rise to the expected outcome, B. We may be sure that the alternatives to hypothesis A which we have conceived will lead to some outcome other than B, but we cannot be sure that there are not still other alternatives, unimagined by us or our colleagues, which would lead to precisely the same outcome as does the one we think we are testing. Hence, the discovery of consequence B does not prove that A is "true."

We can, indeed, have only reasonably good assurance that we have *dis*proved a hypothesis. Suppose that a certain hypothesis, A, must lead to outcome B. Suppose that we have searched diligently under what we conceive to be the appropriate conditions for outcome B and have failed to find it. We may then equate our failure to find the outcome with its non-existence and conclude that our hypothesis, A, is false. However, there is always the possibility that what we fail to find does indeed exist but was sought in the wrong place or by the wrong means.

The Structure of the Natural Sciences

The improbability of obtaining definitive proof or disproof suggests that it might be wise, for purposes of teaching, to treat science not as a process of proof or verification at all but rather as a process of discovery, a process of disclosing events in nature and of discovering ways of relating these events to one another in such a fashion that our understanding is enhanced. In any case, we cannot avoid the realization that science is a process of *constructing* bodies of *tentative* knowledge, of discovering *different* ways of making data coherent, and "telling" about a given subject matter. Ultimately, the test of such tentative bodies of knowledge concerns their usefulness—their usefulness in practice, their usefulness in satisfying our demand for a coherent account, their usefulness in leading to further enquiry.

We turn now to Step Two of the schoolbook version of science, the formation of a hypothesis. In one very large class of short-term enquiries the discrimination of such a step is entirely justified. Consider the physicist who supposes the existence of a minute particle that by definition is inaccessible to observation. Consider the later physicist who assigns to some of these particles a "spin" of a certain speed and direction. Consider the biochemist who constructs a model of the possible structure of the gene. Such hypotheses are "black box" hypotheses in the sense that they are, either by definition or by the limitations of existing techniques, inaccessible to immediate observation. If they are to be "verified" in any sense at all, it must be by the discernment of outcomes and consequences of the matter hypothesized.

Further, each such hypothesis represents a major act of constructive imagination. The scientist takes account of a vast variety of data which must be accounted for. He treats each datum as a limitation on what may be conceived as accounting for the whole range of data, and within the boundaries of these complex limitations he conceives a solution to the problem. Many important researches, especially in the physical sciences, are pursued through the use of such "black box" hypotheses. For such enquiries, we have every reason to discriminate the formation of a hypothesis as a distinct step or act, a step intrinsic to the method used in these researches.

Consider, however, another large class of enquiries. An investigator notes that the pancreas secretes digestive enzymes in large quantities into the small intestine only when food is present in the small intestine. He wishes to determine how the pancreas is stimulated to secrete at the appropriate time. Past knowledge teaches him that the two most likely means are nerve connections from intestine to pancreas or the secretion by the wall of the small intestine of a hormone that is carried by the blood to the pancreas. He looks for such nerve connections and finds them. He tries to extract such a hormone from the intestinal wall and succeeds. The nerve he locates is anatomically discernible and when stimulated at the intestinal end can be shown to convey an impulse to the pancreas. The hormone he extracts is capable of being analyzed chemically, even of being synthesized. Shall we say that the search for such a nervous connection or for such a hormone is instigated by "the formation of a hypothesis"? We may if we wish. If we do, however, we should distinguish between "black box" hypotheses and these "glass box" affairs that refer to things or events that are immediately (or almost immediately) accessible to observation. Further, we should note that because they are accessible to observation, these "glass box" hypotheticals and the processes of enquiry which lead up to them and follow from them differ markedly from those of the "black box" variety. Our biologist *saw* nerve fibres leading to the pancreas; he *saw* that the small intestine and the pancreas were well supplied with blood vessels. His "verification" involved no painful search for consequences that would permit application of some version of the hypothetical syllogism. Rather, he needed only to suppress one of the two possible pathways to determine whether the pancreas still secreted. Better still, he could locate nerve fibres whose stimulation led to pancreatic secretion or isolate a substance from the small intestine which led to pancreatic secretion when injected into the blood.

The importance of noting that such "glass box" hypotheses exist lies in the fact that their transparency, both as to possibility and to verification, makes the isolation of hypothesis-making as a discrete, named step pretentious and over-emphatic. In such cases it is enough to say that the investigator poses the *problem,* "to determine whether the intestinal walls secrete a hormone which stimulates the pancreas." This permits recognition of a pattern of enquiry in which hypotheses, though present in some formal sense, are dim. Thus, we make way for the protests by scientists in certain fields that they make no hypotheses but only observe. Investigators in these fields are much better described as trying to "find out what organ is present," "what animals occupy a given region," "what happens when food is present in the intestines," etc. Such investigators are *looking for* rather than *testing*. In brief, we see again a sense in which science is a process of discovery rather than of proof.

Perhaps the most revealing weakness of the schoolbook version of enquiry is its omission of a step preceding Step One. Step One refers to the discrimination of relevant data but fails to tell us in what way relevance and irrelevance are determined. It further fails to take account of the fact that data are relevant to something, that "relevance" must have a reference. What then are these "relevant" data relevant to and how can we tell when they are?

The answers to these questions require us to recognize the existence of substantive structures and one of the roles they play as principles of enquiry. The role in question is that of giving us our problems for enquiry. We saw one example of this in Chapter 1, where the conception of "tropism" guided early enquiries into animal behavior. Let us take a further case in point. An anatomist, let us suppose, has just completed a re-examination of the adrenal gland. It had formerly been supposed that this part of the body was homogeneous. The anatomist has just discovered that it is made of two distinct kinds of tissue to which he has given topographical names—cortical tissues and medullary tissues. A physiologist reads the anatomist's report of his study and remembers the "function" that has been assigned to this gland. Immediately he says to himself, "In all probability this function is not one function but two. I shall determine where the dividing line is and which function belongs to which tissue of the adrenal gland." He goes to the laboratory, removes the adrenal cortex from a number of animals, leaving the medulla intact; from others he removes the medulla, leaving the cortex intact. Eventually, he and his colleagues succeed in discriminating the function into two and of assigning each to different tissues of the adrenal gland.

What is important here is, first, that this enquiry was initiated, not merely by the gathering of "relevant data" but by the recognition of a *problem*. It was the question "What are the functions of the adrenal cortex and of the adrenal medulla?" which made it possible to decide what data were relevant, what further data were wanted, and what experiment to perform. Second, these questions could not have arisen had there not been in the mind of the investigator and in the habits of the science he represented the pattern of enquiry which revolved around the conception of structure and function. In this particular conception of the subject matter (the substantive structure), the living body is a city, a political state; the organs, the servants of this state, are each discriminable anatomical parts; hence, any newly discriminated anatomical part immediately becomes an object of enquiry, an object to which the question addressed is, "What is its function?" In brief, what data are relevant, what further data are wanted, what experiments ought to be performed, are matters determined by a prior act—the formulation of a problem. The problem, in turn, derives from the prevailing substantive structure guiding enquiry in the field, together with such "index phenomena" as point to the proper place to address the problem.

Let us summarize these criticisms and what they imply in a revised version of the schoolbook study of the short-term syntax of the sciences.

1. The formulation of a problem (from juxtaposing a principle of enquiry—a substantive structure—and index phenomena).

2. The search for data that will suggest possible solutions to this problem.

3. Reformulation of the problem to include these possible solutions.

4. A determination of the data necessary to solve the problem.

5. A plan of experiment that will elicit the data desired.

6. Execution of the experiment and accumulation of the desired data.

7. Interpretation of the data by means of the guiding substantive structures together with previous knowledge possessed by the investigator.

THE LONG-TERM SYNTAX OF THE SCIENCES

It would be well to point out why I have called the pattern described above the short-term syntax of the sciences, or the syntax of stable enquiry. The enquiries that fit this pattern— and they constitute the vast bulk of scientific enquiries—are stable in the sense that their authors think they know exactly what to do. There is no wavering about what questions to ask or what substantive structures to employ. If the current principles of physiology are organ and function, the stable researcher in physiology busies himself discovering the function of first one organ and then another. If the conception of unit gene is the going conception in genetics, the stable enquirer in that field tries to find how many genes and which ones control each of a number of identifiable traits.

Such enquiries are short-term in the sense that separate problems can be pursued separately; each such problem, such as the function of organ X, can be settled in a relatively short time. The substantive structures are accepted as if they were eternal principles; organs obviously exist; equally obviously, each organ has a function. There is no upsetting of the apple cart by asking whether the organism is well understood in terms of organ and function or better understood in some other way. The principle guides the enquiries but is never, itself, the subject of an enquiry.

The syntax of fluid enquiry or the long-term syntax of sciences arises when what the short-term enquirer takes for granted is treated as a problem. The moving force behind fluid enquiry is the demand for increasing validity of substantive structures. Let us recall how we defined validity in Chapter 1. We said there that the criterion of validity demands that the substantive structure, which points to the problems and the data of enquiry, reflect, as much as possible, the richness and complexity of the subject matter to which it is applied. We said also that as investigations proceed under the guidance of one or another substantive structure, we begin to detect inconsistencies and disparities of various sorts. Suppose, for example, that we have developed our physiology under the guidance of a very simple substantive structure. This structure, a simple version of the notion of structure and function, dictates a simple experimental pattern in which we remove an organ and try to determine what aspects of the behavior of the entire organism are missing in consequence. Suppose that by this experimental pattern we have determined that organ X has function A, while organ Y has function B. Then, by accident or design, an experimenter removes both organ X and organ Y from the same animal, only to discover that the result is something far different from the expected mere sum of the losses of function A and function B. Here, then, is a startling disparity between what is expected on the basis of the substantive principle and what is actually disclosed. In other cases, the inconsistency may be between two different bodies of data. Suppose, for example, that removal of organ X under one set of circumstances leads to the conclusion that it performs function A. The removal of the same organ from animals under different living conditions discloses, apparently, the presence of another function, B.

In either case, there appears to be something wrong with the substantive structure, something inadequate relative to the subject matter itself, a failure of complete validity. Our organism turns out to be more complicated than the structure supposes it to be. In the case of the first disparity (between two organs removed separately and the two removed together), we discern a degree of *interaction* between organs which our principle does not include. In the second instance (where removal of the same organ under different circumstances yields evidence pointing to different functions), we see the possibility that even if, as we supposed, organs perform certain functions, the organs may be more flexible as to function than our principle has led us to believe.

When such disparities occur—and they occur periodically in all the sciences—they instigate a new kind of enquiry. We call it fluid enquiry for the obvious reason that matters are no longer fixed and stable in the science. Its underpinnings, its basic principles, are called into question, and a new set of principles, and their test are required. We call it long-term syntax because, in a sense, it is a form of enquiry that proceeds through each and every stable enquiry that takes place in the science. For, if scrutinized in the right way, every attempt to put the question dictated by a given principle of enquiry is a test of that principle. Each such stable enquiry is likely to have its incoherencies and inconsistencies, which are ignored or explained away in the interest of the conduct of the stable enquiry. Thus, for example, the primitive experiment on the role of the nucleus in the cell yielded inconsistencies of data, with respect to what cells died and how quickly, and which cells lived longer, which were "washed out" in the interest of pinning down some role of the nucleus. In other hands or under other circumstances these same disparities might have become the most relevant of the data involved, pointing to the possible inadequacy of the very notion of single, unchanging roles for cellular parts.

The fluid enquirer has three aims: first, to be alert to the moments of enquiry which reveal inadequacies of principle; second, to obtain such clues as he can from current stable enquiries which will point to the specific weakness or inadequacy that characterizes the principle in question; finally, to devise a modification of the existing structure, or a new structure to replace it, that will embrace more of the richness of the subject matter and take account of the specific weaknesses discovered in the older principles.

Since stable enquiries constitute the bulk of enquiries, they also absorb the attention of most scientists most of the time in any given field. In consequence, fluid enquiry is not equally well recognized among all sciences as the important affair it is. Indeed, there are some scientists (if not some sciences) who would deny the very existence of fluid enquiry because they deny the existence of conceptual frames (substantive structures) as underpinnings of their work. Many men feel much more emotional stability and readiness for work if they permit themselves to believe that the notions that guide their work represent "the facts" and are stable and eternal. It was once possible to maintain the fantasy of such stability for a lifetime. Relatively few men were engaged in research, and research itself was not an organized enterprise. Substantive structures, in consequence, had a long life; and the interval between revisions was often longer than the lifetime of a generation of scientists. This is no longer the case. Scientific enquiry is a vast and organized enterprise, and revisions of principle occur frequently. As a result, we find fluid enquiry accorded great honor in some sciences and in others, recognition, at least. The theoretical physicist is a man of honor in his field. The chemical physicist is recognized and rewarded for his contributions to fluid enquiry in the field of chemistry. Even in biology a grudging recognition of the necessity for fluid enquiry has appeared within the last ten years.

It is virtually impossible to provide a step-by-step description of the method of fluid enquiry, for, while stable enquirers permit themselves some flexibility in the interpretation of data, there is practically no limit to the flexibility with which the fluid enquirer may work. The detection of inadequacies in current structures is an act of creative "insight" which has no known method. The revision of a structure or the invention of a new one is an act of creative imagination for which, again, there are no known methods. Even the timing, the occasion, for fluid enquiry is indefinitely variable. In one case, a courageous man, Edward Murray East, undertook a piece of fluid enquiry well before there was general recognition of any need for it. In the years between 1900 and 1914, the newly opened study of heredity was doing very well with a simple conception of the hereditary trait and the hereditary unit. The ruling conception dictated the recognition of hereditary traits as "either/or" phenomenon. One had blue eyes or brown eyes. One had curly hair or straight hair, and so on. The conception of the unit of heredity, the gene, was similarly either/or. One had gene A or one had its substitute gene *a* (and in unusual cases a third or a fourth substitute), but whether the alternatives were one or several, one had or did not have a given gene. There were no bits of genes. The effect of this simple conception of trait and genetic unit was such that the study of hereditary patterns was apparently limited to the study of traits that could be distinguished as either/or. The possibility of accounting for such "continuously variable" traits as height, weight, number of rows of kernels on an ear of corn, and so on, was remote. Yet, at this time, there were still plenty of either/or traits to be investigated and only a few men were particularly worried about the limitations of the existing conceptual structure. Yet, in 1916, East published papers on the inheritance of size and on the inheritance of rows of kernels of corn, papers that were designed to exhibit the way in which the conception of the gene and its action could be so modified as to make possible the study of such continuously variable traits. By contrast, many other revisions of conceptual structure took place only when the need was desperate.

We said above that there are three objectives of fluid enquiry: detection of the inadequacy of a conceptual structure, identification of its particular weaknesses, devising of replacements. In fact, there is a fourth objective of fluid enquiry which shares with these three their "fluidity," their flexibility of method, but which is much more open to study than acts of creative insight or imagination. This fourth objective consists of the political-rhetorical-scientific hard work of obtaining acceptance of a new conceptual scheme by one's fellow scientists. This task, political-rhetorical though it be, is as much a part of the scientific enterprise as obtaining data, or persuading one's colleagues that one's interpretation of data is appropriate.

When new conceptual structures are proposed in the intellectual marketplace of science, four major criteria are usually brought to bear by the community of scientists in determining whether or not to accept the proposed new structures. I have given commonplace names to these criteria as follows: adequacy, interconnectivity, feasibility, and continuity. As we shall see, these criteria are often in conflict or tension with one another in the sense that maximizing one of them may be achievable only by minimizing another. Since the criteria often are in competition, the fact that they also tend to reflect widely differing preferences on the part of different scientists leads to an even more complex and unpredictable patterning of fluid enquiry than we have already suggested. Let us look briefly at each of these criteria.

The "adequacy" of a proposed new principle refers to its most obviously needed characteristic—its ability to establish such connections *within* the subject matter that the incoherencies and inconsistencies exhibited by the use of earlier principles will be repaired. For example, to be an adequate successor to the principle of the simple conception of structure and function described earlier, a principle would have to enable us to conceive of interactions among organs and among their functions, together with an even higher level of interaction which would lead to detection of and response to changes in the environing state of the organism. More specifically, we would need to make our conception of the anatomy and physiology of an organism so flexible that we could investigate the possibility that one organ, responding to a change in the environment, so affected a second organ that the second one underwent a change in its fine structure leading to a change in its activity which made it a more helpful contributor to the over-all economy of the body under the new conditions. Few scientists would underestimate the importance of the criterion of adequacy in judging a proposed new conception. Yet, in its application, many may prefer a less adequate conception as a price worth paying for obtaining greater "continuity."

The criterion of continuity brings into sharp relief the operation of conservatism in science. Clearly, the advantages of a radically new conception lie in the future—enquiries not yet undertaken and bodies of knowledge not yet envisaged. Anxiety is roused in many scientists by considering such a radical change. Furthermore, there is ground for anxiety since a radical departure is bound to be a costly affair. The old body of knowledge will require extensive reformulation. There must be sweeping rewriting of textbooks and reorganization of courses and training programs for graduate students. Much of this work may fall on the shoulders of those who were responsible for the development of the bodies of knowledge now scheduled for oblivion. Little wonder then that such radical proposals may often be resisted on the ground that sufficient advance could be made in enquiry with principles far less radical, that is, with principles exhibiting much more unity of content and connection with the principles being discarded. It is this view that I summarize under the heading of "continuity."

Where the criterion of adequacy refers to the richness of

connection which a new structure establishes among elements or parts *within* a subject matter, interconnectivity refers to the extent and richness of connection which new conceptions promise to establish *between* subject matters formerly held separate. This criterion is emphasized by scientists who are concerned with the unification of science, for, obviously, conceptions that establish connections among subject matters lay a ground for enquiries that cover them both at once and therefore promise unification of what was formerly two bodies of knowledge. Newtonian mechanics is a case in point in that it established connection between terrestrial and celestial motions. John Dalton's "A New System of Chemical Philosophy" contains a similar emphasis on the criterion of interconnectivity. His argument for an atomic concept as the guiding principle for chemical enquiry emphasizes again and again the point that such a principle would relate the subject matter of chemical analysis and synthesis to problems of falling bodies, the planets, and the motions of bodies generally, through its connection with the dynamical conception of force.

The criterion of feasibility shares the conservative tendency of the criterion of continuity. When new conceptual structures are proposed, they are proposed as *working* principles: they must lead to enquiries that can be carried out within the limitations of existing techniques, skills, and facilities. Yet they normally call for new experimental patterns, for unfamiliar forms of data, for new ways of collating and arranging data, even for new technical devices. Hence, proposed new principles are scrutinized closely to determine the relative ease, cost, precision, and reliability with which the data they require can be collected and analyzed. A principle will be resisted if the cost of putting it into operation is extremely high or if there is no clear promise of the desired degree of precision and reliability. Consequently, many defenses of new structures do not appear to be primarily proposals of new conceptions at all. Rather, they are reports of experiments actually performed and data actually collected, the data and the experiments being those evoked by a new conception. The point, of course, is to make clear by example rather than by argument the feasibility of the principle in question.

Joseph J. Schwab

As we have said, these several criteria are applied differently by different men at different times. There is sometimes quick success of radically new, highly adequate, or interconnecting principle. At other times, the shift of principle is mild indeed, hewing closely to the criteria of continuity and feasibility. In all cases, however, the shift of principle re-energizes enquiry in the field and gives it new directions.

SUBSTANTIVE STRUCTURES

If it is difficult to sketch the course of fluid enquiry, it is impossible to describe the substantive structures of the sciences in general. These structures are not only extremely numerous but extremely varied. They are so because of the very character of substantive structures and the role they play. They are designed to fit given subject matters as known at a given moment of their investigation. And whether these subject matters differ from one another *sub specie eternitatis,* or only appear to differ because previous principles for enquiry into them have differed, is beside the point; they do differ. As a result, the substantive structures used in psychology belong to psychology and differ radically from those appropriate to biology, physics, or chemistry. We can, however, sketch briefly a few of the forms or shapes that principles in the sciences can take on.

Many of the effective principles in the sciences have been of a kind we may call *reductive.* Reductive principles instruct the enquirer to treat his subject matter as something that takes on all its important properties from its own elements or parts and from the connections relating these parts to one another. Thus the properties of the larger whole are accounted for by the summations, combinations, and interactions of the constitutive parts. The principles of nineteenth-century chemistry provide a case in point. First, these principles instructed the chemist to treat the subject of his enquiry as compounds of material, chemical elements. Second, these principles then provided means for identifying and distinguishing one element from another and for distinguishing an element from a compound. Third, the same principles included a conception of binding factors (affinities or valences) which established investigable relations among elements in compounds. Thus chemical sub-

46

stances are *reduced* to simple chemical substances and connections between them. In the same way, early atomic physicists reduced the 92 kinds of chemical atoms to two or three kinds of smaller physical "atoms." Early psychologists developed the same sort of reductive principle. The complex of behavior was reduced to simple combinations of learned and unlearned units of behavior (conditioned and unconditioned reflexes).

Of course, the sort of unit or element and the kind of connection between them which are used in reductive principles vary with the subject matter. It is a far cry from the psychical elements (id, ego, and super-ego) of the Freudian theory of personality to the 92 elements of nineteenth-century chemistry. There are even very important differences between the 92 chemical elements and the elemental particles of early twentieth-century physics. Nevertheless, all such structures have this in common: some chosen whole is understood, "explained" in terms of (a) its particular constituents, and (b) the relations that bind these constituents together in a certain way. Meanwhile, the constituents themselves go unexplained. They are the irreducible elements, invariant and independent of one another, which simply "are" for the sake of explaining that which they compose.

The second kind of scientific principle we may call "organic" or "holistic." Such principles are superficially the opposite of reductive ones. Where reductive principles instruct us to find our explanation of larger wholes in their constituent parts, organic principles instruct us to treat the larger whole as simply "being" (i.e., not explained). Then, provided with this stability of the whole, we are told to explain its parts by reference to the describable but unexplained whole. This is well illustrated by the kind of common-sense statement which runs, "Cities being what they are, we must expect slums to develop." Or, "Since the State exists to regulate the behavior of its members so as to maximize their well-being, we can now identify the essential function of each of its parts. The legislative part exists to identify the conditions of well-being and to state the rules of behavior which will lead to realization of these conditions, etc."

When such principles are used in sciences, we see, first, that certain wholes are identified, bounded, and described. (They are only described, however, not explained.) Then, various parts of the described whole are discriminated and "explained" in terms of the contribution they make to the bounded whole. Such principles as these are probably even more numerous than reductive principles and give rise to the commonest form of knowledge—classificatory schemes. The operation of such principles is most easily seen in the traditional physiology that first assigns certain fixed activities as descriptive of an organism (e.g., ingestion, digestion, excretion, reproduction) and then describes each part of the organism by reference to what it contributes to one or another of these defining activities. Finally, such principles enable us to classify all sorts of organisms according to the activities they have or do not have and according to the sorts of organs or parts that contribute to each such activity.

Finally, let us take note of still a third form of principle, which we may call "rational" without implying that reductive or organic principles are in any sense irrational. Where, roughly speaking, reductive principles describe wholes in terms of their parts, and organic principles describe parts in terms of their contribution to a whole, rational principles instruct the scientist to treat his subject matter as determined or explained by some system, often some purely mathematical or rational structure of relationships within which the subject matter exists and acts. Take, for example, an early field or gradient theory in embryology. The parts of the developing animal are taken as the subject matter. The laws of their development is the knowledge sought, the "explanation" desired. This knowledge is then sought, not in terms of particular constituent parts, or of the action of particular causes but in terms of the entire environing system created by the interactions of each of these developing parts with every other developing part. When we explain the whole system of the heavens as well as the behavior of any one planet by referring to the properties of ellipses and the consequences of centripetal forces which vary as the square of distance, we have another example of the use of rational principles.

Rational principles usually require a special language. Ordinary language is well suited to analyzing things, taking them apart. On the whole, too, ordinary language is well designed to describe things or the visible behavior of things. Rational principles, by contrast, forbid us to seek explanations by isolating bits and pieces of things, events, or characteristics. They ask us, instead, to talk in terms of an entire system. Furthermore, the system is usually a system of relationships treated apart from the things in the relationship. Thus, the system we are required to deal with is not only a system but an abstract system. We require, then, a language capable of coping with abstract systems. Mathematics is the principal source of such languages. Hence, the knowledge that arises from the application of rational principles is usually formulated in the form of equations, many of whose terms do not refer to simple, measurable, physical quantities.

We should close, I think, by pointing out that some principles arise from the attempt to avoid principles. Two such anti-principles are conspicuous. In the physical sciences we are periodically confronted by the plea to avoid all such conceptual structures as particles and waves, even such accepted notions as force and mass. Instead, say the proponents of anti-principles, we should limit science to the description of measurable, related changes. For example, according to this view we should not assert that $F = MA$ but, rather, only report the different accelerations imparted to a given object by impact from balls of different weights.

In biology we sometimes have recourse to the simple search for the sequence of common events. If we are interested in event A, such as the secretion by a gland, we ask what event Z immediately precedes it, what further event precedes that one, and so on.

L. H. LANGE

•

THE STRUCTURE OF MATHEMATICS

If we look today at almost any field of intellectual activity, we find that it is no longer what it once was. The parts making up that field will, to greater and lesser degrees, be less distinct than they once were. This is supremely true if we look at mathematics. It was once quite near the truth to say that the principal parts of the structure of mathematics were algebra, geometry, and analysis. In looking at a given piece of mathematics, one could very often say that it belonged to a specific area of mathematical inquiry, for example, geometry, and one could often say correctly that its author was principally a geometer. This is no longer quite the case. While it is certainly true that a mathematician today should be competent in algebra, geometry, and analysis, the mathematical profession today insists that he achieve a more comprehensive and integrated view of mathematics. The profession will insist that he attain a rather more sophisticated view of mathematics, that he understand that the word "structure" has a central meaning and position in this field. For here one asks of a particular mathematician, "What structures does he study?" Often, the answer will show that the man's work with certain structures cannot be labeled as geometry, or algebra, or analysis, but rather shows new insights into parts of all of them. Today, more than ever before, the parts of mathematics are related by this search for common, comprehensive abstract structures. This we shall try to make clearer, while insisting that it is not the whole story.

Mathematicians, on the whole, have been reluctant to give their blessings to deep philosophical inquiries into the nature

The Structure of Mathematics

of their field. Most members of the mathematical community—it is a remarkably worldwide community, possessing a universality uncommon in other areas of human enterprise—would prefer to *do* mathematics, not concern themselves excessively with the question of what it is that they are doing. History, and fairly recent history, has witnessed antagonism on the part of mathematicians to such inquiry. This can be understood to an extent, for it is impossible even to find a widely accepted single definition of mathematics. I hold with those who maintain that it is active involvement and experience in mathematics—in the creation and development of it—not just philosophy, which enables a person to find a meaningful and acceptable working definition of what mathematics is.

What Is Mathematics?

Some have said that "mathematics is what a mathematician does"—this "definition" has its appeal—but mathematicians are human beings. They eat and sleep, love and hate, have passions and display humor, engage in "publicationmanship," often solve fairly trivial problems in fairly grand ways, participate heatedly in politics, and, strange as it may seem, though they spend their lives in a field that is accepted as a model of all our intellectual enterprises, cannot be counted on to be coolly reasonable in the affairs of daily life.

I confess that I share with most mathematicians the feeling that I'd much rather write mathematics than write about mathematics. I'd rather write an exposition of a piece of worthwhile mathematics than to risk losing myself and the reader in a discussion too broad and too filled with words having perhaps too little of a concrete ring to them. In connection with this observation, I have a chance to repeat an ancient anecdote. (Dr. Robert Oppenheimer tells it, and he says it is ancient.) There was an old professor of biology who, over the years, consistently asked Ph.D. candidates to tell him all they knew about worms. Candidates, of course, studied worms. Then, alas, one day he asked the candidate to tell him all about elephants. The candidate answered, "The elephant is a very large animal. It has a wormlike trunk. Now, worms may be divided into the following three classes. . . ."

L. H. Lange

What is mathematics? What is the place of mathematics in the scheme of things? Does it say anything about God? About Man? On these latter two questions I'll only say that a religious person can, if he wishes, find much enlightened solace in it, and so can the humanist. (Mathematicians know well the feelings of the religious Euler on the one hand, and of the atheistic Laplace, on the other.) I am aware of the fact pointed out by Sir Edmund Whittaker[1] when he wrote, "Curiously enough, I do not remember ever having seen a sustained argument by any author which, starting from philosophical or theological premises likely to meet with general acceptance, reached the conclusion that a praiseworthy ordering of one's life is to devote it to research in mathematics." It is true, however, that there are harmonies in mathematics which, if they found their way into the broader life of man, could only lead to various ameliorations. Furthermore, it is true that mathematics is a supreme tool for liberating ourselves from metaphysical prejudices.

What is mathematics? A partial definition is this: It is the study of abstract forms and structures and the relations among them. Mathematicians will see mathematical relations everywhere, concrete illustrations of abstract models which they study. Musicians, I am sure, hear music everywhere. Criminologists see crime everywhere. Mathematicians and scientists will see applications of mathematics everywhere, but mathematicians primarily study structures, abstract structures. It was Poincaré who said that mathematics is the "art of giving the same name to different things." This comes very close to being satisfactory, but, as I shall point out, the study of structures and theorems about them is not the whole story of mathematics. It is true that the latter-day (meaning: time since the latter part of the nineteenth century) emphasis on abstractness and critical, logical procedures has taught us that many of the very great contributions to knowledge made by mathematics are the result of an insistence on the dissubstantiation of the concepts studied by mathematicians. I shall try to give a modern meaning to Poincaré's definition and the remarks just made. Furthermore, I shall try to say something about some comparatively recent

[1] *Scientific American* (September 1950), p. 42.

results which have non-trivial philosophical implications. I shall insist, however, that structural studies are not the whole story; that the deduction of theorems from a minimal set of postulates is not all. If it were, then I am sure that many intelligent human beings would steer clear of mathematics. This would be bad, and I am convinced that if larger numbers of our fellow human beings would take up the challenge of mastering some mathematics and some of the spirit of modern mathematics, they and our society as a whole would win a prize of great worth.

Some Old Mathematics

Here, first, are some examples of some old mathematics. Who would say that they are not also examples of good mathematics? Certainly, those who have created some mathematics and have cultivated a reverence for its history will not disparage these examples.

I understand that a figure somewhat like the following one appeared in a very old book in India. The caption asked simply that the reader "Behold!"

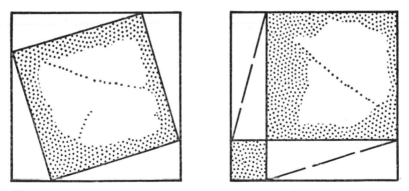

Figure 1

It is unfair of me to tell the reader immediately what the picture says, but I must. It tells us about one of the most famous and important theorems in mathematics, the Pythagorean Theorem: the sum of the areas of the squares on the two legs of any right triangle equals the area of the square on the hypotenuse of that triangle.

Is it a proof? Does the reader doubt the result? I am sure he does not, and I am further convinced that most people would be impatient and bored with an exposition of the many details of a careful proof of the proposition.

Here is another example from ancient mathematics. It, too, deals with an important mathematical fact. All of you know that the diameter of a circle is twice its radius in length, and that the circumference of a circle is π times its diameter. What is the area of a circle of radius r? If we did not know the answer, and we took the question seriously, we would naturally try to find an approximate answer, using facts we already do know. Here is a way in which we might proceed. (See Figure 2. It is a bit cluttered, so don't try to take all its features into your consciousness at once. The reader should introduce each feature as it is brought to his attention in the two paragraphs below.)

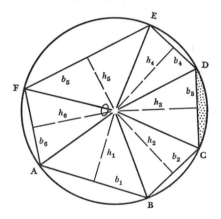

FIGURE 2

Choosing, say, six points A, B, C, D, E, F on the rim of our circle of radius r, we could use the resulting line segments, of lengths b_1, b_2, . . . , b_6 as bases of six triangles, each having its apex at O, the center of our circle. We seek a positive number, α, which can reasonably be assigned the distinction of measuring the area of our circle. We do not know α, but surely the sum of the numbers that measure the areas of our six triangles gives us a first (under) approximation to α. Let us call this approximating sum, s_6. We see that $0 < \alpha - s_6$, i.e., $\alpha - s_6$ is a positive number. Now, $\alpha - s_6$ is the number that represents the error in our approximation to α. This error is associated with six portions in our figure, the portions like the shaded one, the portions outside our triangles but inside our circle. How could we get a better approximation to α? (Remember, we seek α, passionately, impatiently!) Of course! Get a figure in which "those shaded portions" aren't so big! How? Well, choose more than six points on the rim, and choose those points so that the resulting b's are smaller.

That's what we'll do, but first let's calculate s_6. This is quite simple, for after introducing the altitudes $h_1, h_2, \ldots h_6$, we see that

$$s_6 = \tfrac{1}{2} b_1 h_1 + \tfrac{1}{2} b_2 h_2 + \ldots + \tfrac{1}{2} b_6 h_6,$$

which, by the way, a mathematician would write as

$$s_6 = \sum^{6} \tfrac{1}{2}\, b_k\, h_k.$$

Now let's pursue our plan for obtaining a better approximation to α. This time we could choose, say, twenty points on the rim of our circle in such a way that the resulting shaded portions would have a total area less than we observed in the previous case. This we can certainly do. For simplicity—and everybody likes simplicity—we could have stipulated at the beginning that when we choose our rim-points, we'll always have them equally spaced about the circumference. Then if we had n rim-points, we'd have n altitudes: $h_1, h_2, \ldots, h_n$, and these would all be equal in size, $h_1 = h_2 = \ldots = h_n$. The sum of the areas of the resulting n triangles would be $s_n = \tfrac{1}{2} b_1 h_1 + \ldots$ $\tfrac{1}{2} b_n h_n = \tfrac{1}{2} h_n (b_1 + \ldots + b_n)$. Now, as we continue this process, taking larger and larger values of n, we could never get the number α as one of our sums, but we can get as close to it as anyone could require, with this impossibility in mind, no matter how finicky he may be. That is, given any positive allowable error, ε, we are sure there exists an N such that $0 < \alpha - s_N < \varepsilon$, i.e., the difference between α and our resulting approximation s_N is less than ε. If, now, we chose more than N rim-points in the manner we've agreed on, we'd get still better approxima-

L. H. Lange

tions, and our approximations would get closer and closer to just one number, namely α. (A sequence of this sort could not, of course, get closer and closer to two, or more, numbers. This is not only obvious—it happens also to be true.) Hence, not knowing α, we ask ourselves what happens to s_n as n gets larger and larger. Well, $s_n = \frac{1}{2} h_n (b_1 + b_2 + \ldots + b_n)$. Now, as n gets larger, we find that h_n gets closer and closer to the value r— Do you agree? See Figure 2.—and the sum $b_1 + b_2 + \ldots + b_n$ gets closer and closer to the circumference, namely $\pi (2r)$. Thus s_n approaches $\frac{1}{2} (r) (\pi \cdot 2r) = \pi r^2$, and this must be α.

Do you doubt that this proves the result $\alpha = \pi r^2$? Well, you may be permitted a few more misgivings than you might have had in our first example—the one involving the Pythagorean Theorem. It is true that if we were to act on some of the puzzlements that might occur to us here, we'd be led to some rather deep and important mathematical questions and possibly answers. But I doubt that you question the result, really.

At this time, permit me to remark that there are levels on which questions are asked. There are levels of proofs. True, one should not deceive his students. It is a disservice to make calculus—incidentally, we just experienced some rudimentary calculus—or algebra or geometry too easy and slipshod. One must learn to produce polished questions and polished answers. No, one must not deceive. Nor, on the other hand, should one get bogged down forever, and at the wrong times, in unnecessary detail. It would be wrong to say unwanted detail at this point. This is where teachers come in—and no book can really serve. Students must be taught to question, for they may not know what is wanted or what is wanting. They can learn to question. This the teacher must teach. He must also lead them to observe many beautiful and important mathematical facts in many areas of mathematics, and this can't take forever. He must not, when he teaches rigorous, careful, logical procedure, deprive his students of their intuition! He must not deprive them of their intuitive adventurousness. He must not deprive them of their natural inductive capacities. For it may be the inductive thinkers who are most important to society. In this connection it should be pointed out that mathematicians know in their bones that the distinguished Professor Pólya, of Stanford, is correct when he continues to insist, in various ways, that theorems must be guessed before they can be proved.

I wish to show the reader quickly and without any pretense at a derivation, another beautiful old result in mathematics, so striking that it was carved on the stone that marked the grave of its discoverer, Archimedes (died 212 B.C.), who derived it using methods that are not unrelated to those in our second example. It is illustrated in Figure 3.

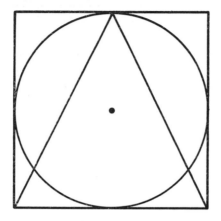

FIGURE 3

Archimedes showed that if one rotates this figure about an axis that bisects it vertically, and if the resulting cone holds one gallon of water, then the resulting sphere will hold two gallons, and the resulting cylinder will hold three!

I could go on like this, exhibiting numerous beautiful results in older but still important mathematics, using various "economical demonstrations" and leaving various puzzlements scattered about the landscape, puzzlements that mathematicians take quite seriously. (Other examples are:

$$\sum_{m=1}^{\infty} \frac{1}{m^2} = \frac{\pi^2}{6}; \quad \prod_p \left(1 - \frac{1}{p^2}\right) = \frac{6}{\pi^2}; \quad e^{i\pi} = -1.)$$

These and other examples can be used to lead into deep investigations in geometry, in the theory of numbers, in calculus, and in the structure of the system of real numbers.

L. H. Lange

SOME SLIGHTLY NEWER MATHEMATICS

I must proceed, however, to an example that illustrates structural considerations in modern mathematics. (To be sure, it is hardly a part of modern modern algebra, a term someone recently coined.) The example is not difficult, is not ancient, is not new. The example will, however, allow me to attempt to give you an insight into what a statement like Poincaré's means to a mathematician today. (Recall, he said that mathematics is the art of giving the same name to different things.) The example concerns the mathematical idea of a group. This idea, the idea of a group, is an example of a type of mathematical structure which may appear in various parts of mathematics—it does indeed appear in algebra, geometry, and analysis. It started in analysis, but its home is in alegbra.

Now, I am reluctant to begin by merely stating the definition of an abstract group. I have been a teacher too long not to know that most of us dislike having a definition cast before us in an unmotivated manner. So just a bit of motivation is in order. Consider the collection, P, of all symbols of the form $\frac{p}{q}$, where p and q are positive whole numbers, having no factors in common. For example, $\frac{4}{9}$ and $\frac{14}{5}$ are members of this set of elements, but $\frac{18}{4}$ is not. So far we have before us merely an amorphous collection of elements with which we are all familiar. Let us now define and consider a familiar multiplication of the members of our collection. Thus $\frac{p}{q} \times \frac{s}{t} = \frac{p \times s}{q \times t}$. Now, when we multiply two members of our set, do we always get a result which is a member of our set, P? The answer is no. For example, $\frac{2}{3} \times \frac{5}{4} = \frac{10}{12}$, and $\frac{10}{12}$ is not a member of P. I don't like this, so I am going to have us consider the set P^* of all symbols $\frac{p}{q}$, where p and q are positive whole numbers. I am going to define the symbol "$=$" by stipulating that we will

58

write $\frac{p}{q} = \frac{s}{t}$ if and only if $p \times t = q \times s$. (Thus, we will write $\frac{10}{12} = \frac{5}{6}$.) Now it is true that "our multiplication is a 'binary composition' on P^*," i.e., if we perform the operation "$\times$" on any ordered pair of elements of P^*, the result is again a member of P^*. We have defined what we shall mean by $a = b$, where a and b are elements of P^*, and we now have a mathematical system $(P^*, \times)$, not merely an amorphous collection of things.

Now the reader already knows a number of facts about the system we are considering. He knows that, for example,

$$\left(\frac{4}{3} \times \frac{2}{5}\right) \times \left(\frac{7}{6}\right) = \left(\frac{4}{3}\right) \times \left(\frac{2}{5} \times \frac{7}{6}\right)$$

He also knows that $\frac{p}{q} \times \frac{1}{1} = \frac{p}{q}$ and that $\frac{p}{q} = \frac{q}{p} \times \frac{1}{1}$. He knows still more about this system. For example, he knows that, $\frac{4}{3} \times \frac{7}{23} = \frac{7}{23} \times \frac{3}{4}$; in fact, he knows that if a and b are any elements of P^*, then $a \times b = b \times a$ holds true.

Enough of motivation. Here is a definition of an abstract group, a certain kind of (simple) mathematical system: An abstract group consists of a set, S, of (undefined) elements, together with a binary composition, $\times$, on S such that

(1) if a and b are members of S, the statement $a = b$ is defined;

(2) if a and b are any members of S, then $a \times b$ is a well-defined element of S;

(3) if a, b, and c are any members of S, then
$$(a \times b) \times (c) = (a) \times (b \times c);$$

(4) S contains an element, i, such that for any element a of S we have $a \times i = i \times a = a$;

(5) for each element a in S, there exists an element a^* in S such that $a \times a^* = a^* \times a = i$.

That is a definition of an abstract group. I hasten to add that an abstract group is called an abelian (or commutative) group, if and only if it is also true that, whenever a and b are any members of S, then $a \times b = b \times a$.

Now, there are many examples of groups in mathematics. I have already given one example and I shall give another. By the way, not all groups are abelian, and I have only recently seen a new proof of the old theorem that no non-abelian group can contain fewer than six (distinct) elements. A significant part of mathematical activity today is the search for newer proofs of old theorems. Mathematicians are not only interested in theorems, they are very interested in how they are proved. They cheer elegant proofs! Here is one point of difference between engineers and mathematicians.

This last remark, concerning non-abelian groups, begins to illustrate a reason for engaging in abstract procedure, a reason for studying structures in the abstract. One does not do this in order to consign known results to an abstract oblivion (though some people may have or give the impression that such is the case!), nor does one do this in order to drive home the point that "correct" reasoning should not be confined to the traditional course in plane geometry. One does not engage in structural studies in order to develop unhelpful elaborations, or to engage in a social conformity motivated by the fact that this sort of procedure seems to have the sanction of our age. We do not do it in order to replace the meaningless calculational drills of yesteryear with newer but nevertheless still meaningless calculational drills today. We engage in the study of abstract structures in order to be comprehensive, to be economical, to obtain considerable results with what ofttimes amounts to very little effort. If we can prove a theorem, a fact, about an abstract group, we automatically know that this theorem holds in any concrete natural instance of such a mathematical system. If we had never defined a group, and consequently never proved a theorem, say Theorem A, about an abstract group, then every time we encountered what amounted to a group in nature, we would have to prove Theorem A all over again. Thus, once an abstract group theory has been developed, once a whole collection of theorems about abstract groups has been collected, we become aware that we are in possession of a great deal of economical scientific power. For, once we recognize that we are faced with an example of a group in some work we are doing,

The Structure of Mathematics

we automatically know a tremendous amount about the system that lies before us.

Perhaps at this point I will not be wrong if I guess that the reader has a glimmering of what Poincaré could have meant when he said that mathematics was the art of giving the same name to different things.

Here is another simple example of a theorem about our abstract group: $(S, \times)$. This time we shall give the proof.

Theorem (A Cancellation Law): If a, b, and c are members of S, then $a \times b = a \times c$ always implies $b = c$.

Proof: Assume $a \times b = a \times c$. Since a is a member of S, there exists an element a^* such that $a^* \times a = i$. Now $a \times b = a \times c$ implies that $(a^*) \times (a \times b) = (a^*) \times (a \times c)$. But this is equivalent to $(a^* \times a) \times (b) = (a^* \times a) \times (c)$, and this, in turn, is equivalent to $(i) \times (b) = (i) \times (c)$. By the nature of the element (i), this yields $b = c$; our theorem is proved.

We could also prove that $b \times a = c \times a$ always implies $b = c$, and we would then also have permission to "right-cancel" in our dealings with any group.

I shall now discuss briefly just one more example of a group. Our first example, $(P^*, \times)$, was a group containing an infinity of elements. (The infinity involved was, by the way, the smallest infinity there is.) The example I shall discuss now is a finite group, a group possessing only eight elements. Furthermore, this one is non-abelian, while our first example involved an abelian group. It is known as the "group of symmetries of the square."

I must first define the set of elements which enters our system. To do this, I need the reader's imaginative help. Sit at your desk and cut a square hole in its top, one-eighth of an inch deep. Now take a square piece of cardboard which fits this hole exactly. Label the corners A, B, C, D; putting the A, for example, on both sides of the same corner. Assume the square is in the position shown in Figure 4.

Now, it is easily seen that there are exactly eight ways in which I could replace the square in its hole after picking it up.

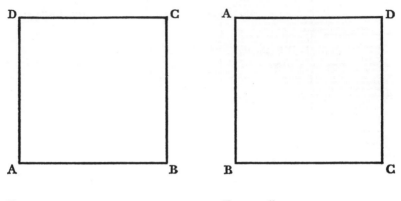

FIGURE 4   FIGURE 5

It is the collection, S, of these eight motions which shall be the set of elements entering our discussion. Thus, if I say that "t is a member of S," I am speaking of a certain motion of this type. I will now assign names, letters, to the elements of S, after which I shall need to define "$a \times b$". Furthermore, we shall let "$a = b$" mean that the motions a and b, when applied to a given position of the square, give the same resulting position of the square.

We now let r be the motion that can be described as a 90° clockwise rotation of our square. That is, r is the motion that takes the square, if it is in the position shown in Figure 4, for example, into the position shown in Figure 5.

Similarly, we let s and t be 180° and 270° clockwise rotations, respectively. We let i be the motion that takes Figure 4, for example, into Figure 4; we let v be the reflection of our square in the vertical bisector of our square hole; h is the reflection in the horizontal bisector; d is the reflection about the right-leaning diagonal; e is the reflection about the left-leaning diagonal.

Finally, we define $a \times b$. We simply let $a \times b$ be the motion that is the result of applying a and then following it with b. Thus, as indicated in Figure 6, we have $r \times v = e$ and $v \times r = d$, showing,

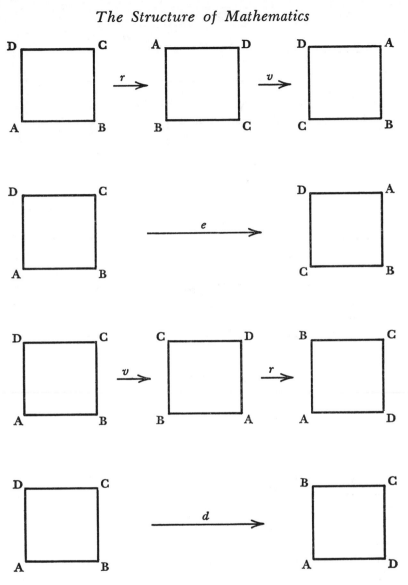

Figure 6

by the way, that $a \times b$ is not always the same as $b \times a$ in our system $(S, \times)$. A complete "multiplication" table is shown in Figure 7. The reader should have no difficulty in reading it.

	i	r	s	t	v	h	d	e
i	i	r	s	t	v	h	d	e
r	r	s	t	i	e	d	v	h
s	s	t	i	r	h	v	e	d
t	t	i	r	s	d	e	h	v
v	v	d	h	e	i	s	r	t
h	h	e	v	d	s	i	t	r
d	d	h	e	v	t	r	i	s
e	e	v	d	h	r	t	s	i

FIGURE 7

Is the system $(S, \times)$ a group? We could proceed to a systematic verification of the fact that this system possesses all the requisite qualities 1–5 (see page 59). We shall not do this at this time—it is left to the reader as an exercise! (Using the table, note that, for example, $(r \times v) \times (s) = (e) \times (s) = d$ and also $(r) \times (v \times s) = (r) \times (h) = d$.) If the reader studies this example, he may agree that it is quite instructive, and he may perceive a deeper understanding of the idea that the word "number" can have many different meanings. In this example, the "numbers," the elements of S, were not those of which our mothers sang in lullabies.

The Structure of Mathematics

(This paragraph is, quite frankly, for those readers who are mathematical specialists. Certainly any discussion of this sort should mention the contemporary importance of the idea of "function." All I wish to say in this connection is that the definition of a function as a "set of ordered pairs" is not quite satisfactory on several counts. If we do wish to be completely rigorous, we should define a function $f: X \to Y$ as a triple (X, Y, S), where S is a certain specified type of subset of $X \times Y$. The mere listing of S does not give all the information required in many investigations, e.g., some algebraic and topological ones. Much more could be written on this, but I leave it at that.)

Much more, of course, can be said about other areas of mathematics. For example, the important and controversial areas of mathematical inquiry which came into being after the work of Peano and Cantor contain mathematical insights which, because of limitations of time, I must only urge the reader to explore. I can say that the "set theory" treated in the schools comes nowhere near the deep and abiding difficulties residing in set theory. The schools treat only set language, and that in a minimal way. I do wish the reader to understand that mathematics has not all been written, by any means, and that there is in mathematics a greater freedom than the "freedom to do the necessary" which characterizes the popular notion of the nature of mathematics.

Some Much Newer Mathematical Work

The reader would do well to investigate the theorems of Gödel (in the 1930's) and the more recent ones of Paul Cohen announced in a colloquium at Stanford on June 6, 1963. These are far-reaching results in the philosophy of mathematics. One of Gödel's theorems says that a formal system of arithmetic, if it is sufficiently rich, will always contain a statement—even a statement of elementary character—which can neither be proved nor disproved. Another says that if such a system is consistent, one can never prove it to be so.

As to Cohen's results, it is perhaps best to bring to the reader's attention the following article, which appeared in the *San Francisco Chronicle* on July 4, 1963.

L. H. Lange

Revolutionary Theory

A MILESTONE IN MATH—
PROFESSOR'S NEW CONCEPT

by: David Perlman
Science Correspondent

A development in mathematics that may profoundly alter man's views of science and philosophy is being discussed with great excitement in Berkeley today.

Only a handful of mathematicians are as yet aware of the development.

But they believe it holds as much promise as the discovery a century ago that men could construct models of space that defied the most basic and ancient premises of Euclid's classical geometry.

The mathematical revolution of the 1830's presaged the new cosmologies of today's astronomers, and prepared the world for Einstein's relativity, as well as much of modern physics.

MILESTONE

It has since been hailed as a milestone in human thought as significant as the Copernican revolution of the 15th century.

Today's development in mathematics is considered to be of similar significance, although its nature is hardly simple.

It is being reported this morning by Dr. Paul J. Cohen, associate professor of mathematics at Stanford University, in a paper presented to an international symposium at Berkeley.

The symposium, attended by nearly 150 mathematicians from more than a dozen nations, deals with the theory of models—a sophisticated discipline probing relationships between the formal structure and the content of mathematical expression.

AXIOM

Back in the days of Euclidean geometry, which ruled the world of math for 2000 years, a basic assumption, or axiom, was the "parallel postulate"—the idea that one and only one line could be drawn through a given point and made parallel to another line.

Mathematicians wondered if this statement could

66

The Structure of Mathematics

be proven, like a theorem, from geometry's other axioms. And when they failed to prove it, the boldest wondered whether it wasn't an independent axiom, which could not be inferred from the rest of Euclidean geometry.

Three famous men—Karl Frederich Gauss, Nikolai Ivanovich Lobachevski and Johann Bolyai—discovered mathematically that the postulate could not be inferred, and that it stood independently. They did it by proposing concepts of "non-Euclidean space," in which Euclid's axiom's were mostly true, but in which the parallel postulate no longer held.

CURVED

In these geometries many parallel lines could be drawn through a given point, because space itself was conceived of as curved.

All this upsetting of applecarts eventually changed the world of geometry, and many conceptions of the physical universe.

In another mathematical field, meanwhile, the theory of sets grew up after it was pioneered by Georg Cantor of Germany in 1870. Like geometry, set theory too has its axioms, or assumptions.

One of these is called the "Axiom of Choice," and it deals with the mathematics of building sets, or collections of objects, out of elements contained in other sets.

WEIRD

Another axiom in set theory is called the "Continuum Hypothesis," it enters a weird world containing many sets of infinite size—such as a collection of all the points on a line, or a collection of all the whole numbers there are.

One of these infinite sets may actually be larger than another, and the continuum hypothesis declares they can be described in order by what are called "trans-finite numbers."

Just as men challenged Euclidean geometry, so today's mathematicians have been trying to prove that these two axioms can be inferred from the other axioms of set theory—or, to reverse it, that they are independent.

Cohen is reporting today that he has succeeded in constructing two new mathematical models. In one all

L. H. Lange

the axioms of set theory hold true, while the axiom of choice alone fails. In the other, all the axioms are true while the continuum hypothesis fails.

In a sense, Cohen has thus constructed a new vision of mathematics, in which the two axioms under question are independent entities. Thus he has done for today's math what the pioneers did for geometry more than a century ago when they constructed their universe of non-Euclidean space.

Three of Cohen's most eminent colleagues hailed his work yesterday.

Said Dr. Andrzej Mostowski of the Mathematical Institute in Warsaw: "It is as though we were living in the time of Gauss; we can see that this discovery has fundamental importance—but we cannot yet foresee its utility."

Professor Leon Henkin of UC, president of the Association for Symbolic Logic, declared: "These new models in set theory may well transform all of algebra and analysis and change science itself."

And Professor Alfred Tarski of UC, the world's leader in the theory of models, added:

"This very profound work will unquestionablv have a great influence in the development of science, although we cannot yet say precisely how.'

Now it is not inordinately difficult to list the important areas and some of the characteristic attitudes in mathematics which teachers must bring to the attention of their students. The difficult problems for teachers and the devisers of curricula are connected with this question: When, at what age or level, should students be introduced to these various ideas and attitudes? Answers to this question require wisdom, balance, historical perspective, and modern insight. The best judges, I am sure, are well-trained teachers of mathematics, persons who know what is important in mathematics, responsible persons who realize that some technical matters may be extremely important to civilization, but may not be important to their students at the time they are their students.

The parts of mathematics, still somewhat properly, though roughly, characterized by the classification "geometry, algebra. analysis" are related by the search for comprehensive theories, comprehensive abstract structures. Creativity in all areas is cherished. Carefully reasoned procedures and developments, together with precision of statement and formulation, are emphasized and demanded. The ideas of set theory and the modern precise notion of function pervade all areas of mathematics, bind them together and, at the same time, make them distinguishable. A sound knowledge of the real number system is essential. In this latter case, as in many others, the more knowledge one possesses concerning concrete mathematical systems, the richer is his understanding of formulated abstract structures. In turn, a rich understanding of abstract structures leads very often to a deeper understanding of concrete systems and the discovery of new theorems, new facts, about them.

Mathematics is a house containing many mansions, and there is room in it for fine human beings. Many mathematicians will apply to themselves what Aristotle said long ago: "The most fortunate of men is he who combines a measure of prosperity with scholarship, research, or contemplation; such a man comes closest to the life of the gods."

Here is a reading list. The books are of varying degrees of difficulty. The titles are, for the most part, self-explanatory, and in each category the first book listed is more elementary than the ones that follow it in the list. An asterisk behind an author's name indicates that the author has a wide reputation as a lucid expositor of mathematics.

1. A pamphlet: *Professional opportunities in mathematics.* Published by the Mathematical Association of America, this pamphlet contains a wealth of information. For information, write Prof. H. Gehman, University of Buffalo, Buffalo, N.Y.
2. *The New Mathematical Library* consists of numerous inexpensive volumes, many of which are very well written. (Random House)
3. *Introduction to the foundations of mathematics* R. L. Wilder, New York, 1952 (Wiley)
4. *Mathematics: the man-made universe* S. K. Stein, San Francisco, 1963 (W. H. Freeman)

L. H. Lange

5. *Philosophy of mathematics and natural science*
   Hermann Weyl, New York, 1963 (Atheneum)
6. *What is mathematics* R. Courant and H. Robbins,
   New York, 1941 (Oxford)
7. *Mathematical discovery* (Two volumes) G. Pólya,*
   New York, 1962 (Wiley)
8. *Induction and analogy in mathematics* G. Pólya,*
   Princeton, 1954 (Princeton)
9. *An introduction to the history of mathematics*
   Howard Eves, New York, 1953 (Rinehart)
10. *Elementary geometry from an advanced standpoint*
    E. Moise, Reading, Mass., 1963 (Addison-Wesley)
11. *Calculus: an introductory approach* I. Niven,*
    Princeton, 1961 (Van Nostrand)
12. *Calculus* (Two volumes) T. Apostol,* New York,
    1963 (Blaisdell)
13. *Advanced calculus* J. M. H. Olmsted, New York,
    1961 (Appleton-Century-Crofts)
14. *A primer of real functions* (A Carus Mathematical
    Monograph) R. P. Boas, Jr., New York, 1960
    (Wiley)
15. *Real analysis* H. L. Royden, New York, 1963
    (Macmillan)
16. *First course in abstract algebra* Richard E. John-
    son, New York, 1953 (Prentice-Hall)
17. *Topics in modern algebra* C. P. Benner, and
    others, New York, 1962 (Harper)
18. *Linear algebra for undergraduates* D. C. Murdoch,
    New York, 1957 (Wiley)
19. *Lectures in abstract algebra* N. Jacobson, New
    York, 1951 (Van Nostrand)
20. *Introduction to topology* B. Mendelson, Boston,
    1962 (Allyn and Bacon)
21. *Introduction to topology and modern analysis*
    G. Simmons, New York, 1963 (McGraw-Hill)
22. *General topology* J. L. Kelley, New York, 1955
    (Van Nostrand)
23. *Naive set theory* P. R. Halmos, Princeton, 1960
    (Van Nostrand)

GRAHAM C. WILSON

•

THE STRUCTURE OF ENGLISH

Man longs for order while the sparks fly upward, and because of this, Jerome Bruner's *The Process of Education*[1] may be a seminal book. In speaking of principles, of structures, of readiness for learning, and of intuition, Bruner is clearly answering our conscious and unconscious demands.

I note in his preface acknowledgments of particular indebtedness to Professor Richard Alpert, until recently a psychologist on the Harvard faculty. Alpert and Dr. Timothy Leary, also formerly of Harvard, have for some time been the most widely known experimenters with the mind-freeing drug LSD. They are the organizers and directors of I.F.I.F., the International Federation for Internal Freedom. Under controlled conditions, they have administered LSD and similar drugs to a large number of people, whenever possible to creative people and to intellectuals. What is universal about the reports of the subjects is that they see forms and patterns. They perceive *everything* as structured.

THE STRUCTURE OF WHAT?

Under the circumstances, it is perhaps unfortunate that I have not been able to take some LSD. Certainly something special is called for to see a concept of over-all structure in English as a discipline in schools and colleges today. To begin with: the structure of what? There is *language,* which may include grammar, philology, anthropology, semantics and general semantics,

[1] Cambridge: Harvard University Press, 1962.

71

psychology, and English as a foreign language; *literature,* which may be English, American, European, world, and, when the time comes, interplanetary; *composition,* which may include grammar (again), rhetoric, semantics (again), and logic. Language artists speak of reading, writing, speaking, and listening. This is quite a mixture. In this age of increasing specialization, it is pleasant to feel that in at least one academic area, the totally qualified teacher will be a true Renaissance man or woman—communicative, comprehensive, contemplative—and nonexistent.

Our discipline is diverse. This diversity results from a historical accident which has created a number of problems, but I do not see that it is in itself bad. "Why," says James Sledd, "should we assume that we can or should unify the group of quite miscellaneous and separately valuable studies that our history has brought together under the name of English?"[2]

I am thinking of some kind of over-all unified structure of the discipline, not just of articulation. It is perhaps articulation that is behind William Riley Parker's recent statement to the Council on Cooperation in Teacher Education:[3]

> Without the least exaggeration I can state that, as a teacher of graduate students in English, there is not one single assumption I can make about either knowledge or skill already acquired. I cannot assume a single book read by everyone in my class. I cannot assume knowledge of the simplest technical term or the simplest Bible story or myth or piece of children's literature. I cannot assume anything except that I have a job which is quite needlessly difficult.

Parker doesn't mean that his students don't know anything—just that they don't know much, and that they know different not muches.

I abandon the possibility of talking about unity among various subject matters, and I will not ask, "Is it bad to teach

---

[2] "In Defense of History," *College English,* XXIV, No. 8 (May 1963), 61.

[3] "The Concept of Structure in 'English,'" delivered to the Council on Cooperation in Teacher Education of the American Council on Education, Washington, D.C., October 20–21, 1961.

The Structure of English

Julius Caesar in the ninth grade if it is to be taught in Fresh-
man English?" I would start with the following: Is there *anything* in our work that has structure in Bruner's sense? Do any
of its parts have a core to which many other things may be related meaningfully? Where, and in what ways, is analogy useful?
Can there be a spiral in what we teach? Is there any significant
transfer from one part of our discipline to another? When are
people ready to learn what?

LANGUAGE AND LITERATURE

I think one can say a few things about these matters, principally
about language and literature. For instance, there is the child's
native language. His linguistic sophistication is sometimes over-
emphasized, but he is certainly a complicated and accurate
linguistic machine. What comes off the top of the child's head
may be ignorant, foolish, or even stupid; but what comes off
the top of his neck is more likely than not to be understandable
without effort to other native speakers of English. This is a
startling achievement, and although we know little about how it
happens, we should exploit the fact that it does happen.

The blessing and the curse of grammar is that it is already
in the head. The appeal to etymology in the search for the real
meaning of a word is frequently foolish, but *education* (from
educare through *educere,* meaning *to lead out*) indicates exactly
what happens in much language study.

A child soon sorts out the sounds of his language. Gleason[4]
says that his daughter early learned to distinguish /p/ or /b/
from /t/ or /d/ and from /k/ or /g/; later she distinguished /p/,
/t/, /k/ from /b/, /d/, /g/, but she still did not distinguish /t/
from /k/. She might, for *cake,* say /teyt/, /keyt/, /teyk/, or even,
in a moment of luck, /keyk/. In other words, his daughter first
distinguished bilabial stops from alveolar and velar stops,
then voiceless stops from voiced ones, and finally separated the
alveolar voiceless stop from the velar voiceless stop. Among
other things, Miss Gleason discovered that language has pattern.

Soon the child controls entire sentence patterns. He may
say, "He brung it home," but he doesn't say, "It brung he

[*] H. A. Gleason, *An Introduction to Descriptive Linguistics* (rev. ed.;
New York: Holt, Rinehart, & Winston, 1961), pp. 258–259.

73

home." He learns about structural meaning. When he hears, "The mirl sooled the pogle," he may not know what all the words mean, but he knows that the pogle got sooled and the mirl did it.

Then he begins to apply a number of linguistic devices—for instance, analogy. From one *cat* he gets two *cats;* from one *dog* he gets two *dogs;* from one *baby* he gets two *babies;* from *cry* he gets *cried;* from *skate* he gets *skated;* from *mad,* he gets *madder* and *maddest;* from *pretty* he gets *prettier* and *prettiest.* And, he gets some other things: from one *child* he gets two *childs;* from one *chaos* he gets two *chaoses;* and from *good* he gets *gooder* and *goodest.* He learns that the language of adults is sometimes seemingly irrational and certainly arbitrary.

The child learns about functional change. He frequently falls *down,* and he watches his father mutter furiously when the 49ers lose the ball on fourth *down.* He knows about derivation. He can turn *act* into *active, friend* into *friendly, marvel* into *marvelous;* he can also turn *cry* into *cryey,* and probably *ouch* into *ouchy*—it being no fault of his that his elders are not consistent.

I don't know just when, but the child must very early realize that languages change. He will become aware of the evanescent nature of some expressions when he—as well as his father—is puzzled by his grandfather's use of *23 skiddoo.*

If he lives in a homogeneous community, he will not hear much dialect variety on the playground, but on the day he goes to first grade, he will have been exposed to 1500 hours of television. He probably knows some Spacespeak, and he may very well have heard the following conversation on the 16th of May, 1963:

MR. COOPER: Fuel is go. Oxygen is go. . . .
Faith is go. She feels real pretty.
MR. SCHIRRA: (in Mercury Control)
You look real go, Gordo. . . .
You're smack dab in the middle of the go block.
MR. COOPER: Boy-oh-Boy!
MR. SCHIRRA: Have a good drive, Bub.
MR. COOPER: Thank you, Buddy.

The Structure of English

Arthur Hoppe of the *San Francisco Chronicle* (May 17, 1963) comments:

> . . . And with these historic words, mankind's latest epic voyage into the vast regions of unchartered space began. . . . I can't help hoping I shall live long enough to see that golden day when America successfully launches the first English-speaking astronaut.

Nevertheless, Mr. Hoppe's boy knows about occupational dialects.

To give our young language expert more credit than he probably deserves, maybe he has even heard a number of politicians on television. If so, he has discovered that some distinguished Americans speak like Senator Fulbright of Arkansas, a onetime Rhodes scholar and now the Chairman of the Senate Foreign Relations Committee, and some like Ambassador Stevenson of Princeton and Illinois, a man so urbane that most Englishmen think he was born in London and smuggled into the United States after he learned to talk. The acceptability of linguistic diversity is a simple fact of a child's experience.

When he enters school, then, a child already knows, in an operational sense, that language has pattern, that language is arbitrary, that language changes, and that language has variety. He knows that it contains methods for changing a word from singular to plural, for increasing intensity, for changing tense, and for changing one kind of word into another kind of word. Although he lacks a technical vocabulary, he knows a good deal about syntax, about usage, about inflection, about comparison, and about derivational processes.

And what happens? What happens is that we take this highly trained, acutely intuitive linguistic machine and treat him in such a way that twelve years later we must give him a text called *Grammar Made Gay* in a desperate, and largely futile, effort to get him to produce sentences that we consider to be literate. This is an unfair statement, since, among other things, it ignores the difference between the spoken language and its written representation. Nevertheless, the point is not irrelevant.

I don't know how to elicit from a student—grade school, high school, or college—a demonstration of his awareness of the kind of linguistic knowledge I have just insisted that he has. But it's there, and we should figure out a way to take advantage of the fact. He has no doubt forgotten about functional change and meaning change by the time he first reads "Dover Beach." The "shingles of the world" will be left at that, because the expression makes a sort of sense, and who would think that shingles could also mean "beach pebbles"? We're likely to take care of his intuition too. We kick the "It's me" out of him, and he is soon full of hyper-urbanisms, revealing not only a new ignorance but a sad self-consciousness. Holden Caulfield of *The Catcher in the Rye,* destined for a sanatorium, is one of the classiest hyper-urbanizers around: "She'd give Allie or I a push." I can only say that the present ferment among linguists and English teachers who spend some time with new approaches in grammar and in teaching language is beginning to produce materials that try to use the knowledge and intuition a student already has.

GRAMMAR

Perhaps it is time to say a word about new approaches to grammar. As every conference-goer now knows, Latin provided the model for traditional grammars of English, as Greek had provided the model for grammars of Latin. This was in some ways unrealistic. The shift from Greek to Latin was not very neat because Latin has no definite article, has a different tense system, and has more cases. English hasn't much of a case system, and inflectionally, anyway, it has only two tenses. The difficulties were solved principally by Procrustes. One of the achievements of contemporary linguistics has been to divest the description of English of its Latinity. Traditional grammar has not, of course, disappeared; there is more than one kind of so-called new grammar, and the difficulty of a Latinate grammar for English was recognized a long time ago, for instance, by John Wallis in *Grammatica Linguae Anglicanae* (1653).

The lag between revelation and acceptance here is considerable. It continues. It has now been more than ten years since the appearance of *The Structure of English* by Fries and *An Outline of English Structure* by Trager and Smith, the two principal books that speeded the adaptation of the materials of the structural linguist to classroom texts, those of Lloyd and Warfel, Paul Roberts, and James Sledd, published between 1956 and 1959.

Transformational grammar for the classroom is even more recent. Noam Chomsky published *Syntactic Structures* in 1957. The first classroom text, Paul Roberts' *English Sentences,* came out in January, 1962. So far as I know, it is the only transformational work ready for the classroom.

I think it makes quite a difference which of the new grammars one emphasizes, but that is not my point here. Some of the assumptions of all linguists direct us to critical areas in the structure of English. Linguists argue. They will continue to argue. Sledd said in 1958, "We are going to disagree for a long time, and when we quit disagreeing, it will be because linguistics is dead."[5] The linguistic battle should be a cause for rejoicing, and not an excuse for waiting around to see how things will come out.

Nevertheless, according to informed estimates of the National Council of Teachers of English, more than 800,000 of the nation's 900,000 elementary, secondary, and college teachers are comparatively uninformed about the nature and structure of the language they teach.[6] A survey by Ingrid Strom reveals that structural grammar is used to some degree by about four per cent of the teachers of English in California and that "about ten percent of the high schools in California have an English teacher who indicated that there are signs of linguistic activity within the English Department." [7] Teachers, including college teachers, knowing anything about transformational grammar are negligible—in number; yet transformational grammar is certainly nearer to what many teachers consider "sound" and

[5] *Third Texas Conference on Problems of Linguistic Analysis in English* (Austin: University of Texas Press, 1962), pp. 176–177.

[6] James R. Squire, " 'Multilevel' Research in English: Imperatives for the Sixties," in *Needed Research in the Teaching of English* (Washington, D.C. U.S. Government Printing Office, 1963), p. 37.

[7] W. Nelson Francis, "The Study of Language in English Teaching," in *ibid.,* p. 46.

"practical" than is structural (immediate constituent) grammar. The similarities of transformational grammar to some of the work of the great historical grammarians—for example, Otto Jespersen—are sometimes striking.

In any event, most of what is taught as grammar in the English classroom is not grammar, but a doctrine of correctness, with a value standard based roughly on the class structure of the United States. I guess there is nothing wrong with this if we just admit that it is so. I certainly would not deny the doctrine of correctness a place in the structure of our discipline. Finding the right word by the application of rules has an ancient and a widespread justification. In the fifth century B.C., Protagoras wrote a book on the correctness of names. The Hindus have a special prayer for the expiation of errors of speech, as do College Board examinees for errors in writing. But we should recognize the doctrine for what it is. Raven McDavid comments of the early United States:[8]

> . . . In the absence of a well-defined elite (except in parts of the South and some of the older cultural centers), it is not surprising that a citizen population that often sought salvation from the literal (though translated) message of the Bible should seek its path to education in the literal message of the school grammars, regardless of the discrepancies between grammatical rules and the actual language practices of the educated. In fact,—for grammar as for morals—the greater that proportion of the erring, the greater the reward of the faithful.

I do not mean that ideas about linguistic choice and a doctrine of correctness are not a part of what we should teach, but they are certainly things of a different conceptual order from the specifics about language that the child picks up more or less unconsciously as a part of the experience of his first few years.

When and how the doctrine of correctness should be applied I cannot say, but if it is tied in with the idea that it is

[8] Raven I. McDavid, Jr., "The Dialects of American English," in W. Nelson Francis, *The Structure of American English*, pp. 510–511. Copyright © 1958 The Ronald Press Company, New York.

possible to maintain in language a *status quo,* it is applying an untenable degeneration theory to language. It is not true that the more a language changes, the poorer it becomes, and it's just as well too, because Karl Dykema has given evidence to show that standard English has been changing more rapidly in the last ten years than it did in earlier decades.[9] There was a time when the relationships among words in an English sentence were indicated by inflection. Today most of our inflections are gone, and we indicate relationships by structure words and by position. It is hard to think of this as the kind of erosion that is erasing meaning.

No one much anymore wants to put case endings back into English, but the ideas that change is likely to be bad and that language may be controlled—language, not an individual's linguistic choice—are ones still held by a great many people. It might be called the hold-the-fort syndrome. It is illustrated in some of the remarkably violent attacks on the third edition of Merriam-Webster's *New International Dictionary.*

However we decide to use the doctrine of correctness in the classroom, we should remember that choice in matters of usage is a value judgment. I feel that in these matters value judgments should be made, and I am perfectly willing to make them for my students. I personally insist upon speaking impeccable English at all times. The fact that my impeccable English forbids *finalize,* however, does not mean that otherwise perfectly acceptable people do not use it as, for instance, Presidents of the United States and Secretaries-General of the United Nations.

The real point here is that we do not discover some day that the kind of English we are trying to teach is not the kind of English we are really used to. I do not know when matters of linguistic taste should first be talked about, but however and whenever they are talked about and taught, they should be made matters of linguistic etiquette and not linguistic law.

COMPOSITION

How does the knowledge of grammar, of linguistic devices, of the principles of correctness affect writing? To R. B. Lees "the

[9] Karl W. Dykema, "How Fast is Standard English Changing?" *American Speech,* XXXI, No. 2 (May, 1956), 95.

major importance of grammatical studies . . . lie[s] in the area of
the so-called behavorial sciences and not in supposed applications to the pedagogy of rhetoric. . . ." [10] Charlton Laird feels
that applied linguistics still has to demonstrate that it can sup-
plant rhetoric.[11] He's right. And so does the extensive use of
grammar of any kind in the teaching of writing. One may, as
Schlegel did, cry, "Read, read. Throw your grammars in the
fire." Indeed, Dwight Burton tells us

> . . . Tentative results from a study carried out in a high
> school in Sudbury, Massachusetts, under a grant from
> the Fund for the Advancement of Education, indicate
> that quantity of reading contributes more impor-
> tantly to improvement of written composition than
> amount of practice in writing, especially among able
> students.[12]

Nevertheless, the hard boundaries that many observers of
the language may see between grammar and composition seem
to be softening a little as scholars give more attention to the
classroom applications of linguistic findings to composition.
Structure is where you find it. Josephine Miles has developed a
morphology of the sentence.[13] Professor Miles refers to Zellig
Harris's *Methods in Structural Linguistics*.[14] Francis Christensen
puts grammar to work in the cause of rhetoric in his "A Genera-
tive Rhetoric of the Sentence." [15] He writes:

> Addition and direction of movement are structural
> principles. They involve the grammatical character of
> the sentence. Before going on to other principles, I
> must say a word about the best grammar as the founda-

[10] Robert B. Lees, "The Promise of Transformational Grammar," *The
English Journal*, LII (May 1963) 345.

[11] Charlton Laird, "Rebuttal," *College English*, XXIV, No. 5 (Febru-
ary 1963), 407.

[12] Dwight L. Burton, "Some Important Research Gaps in the Teaching of Secondary School English," in *Needed Research, op. cit.*, p. 17.

[13] "What We Compose," *Journal of the Conference on College Composition and Communication*, XIV, No. 3 (October 1963), 146–154.

[14] Chicago: University of Chicago Press, 1951.

[15] *Journal of the Conference on College Composition and Communication*, XIV, No. 3 (October 1963), 155–161.

tion for rhetoric. *I cannot conceive any useful trans-actions between teacher and students unless they have in common a language for talking about sentences.* [Italics added] The best grammar is the grammar that best displays the layers of structure of the English sentence. The best I have found in a textbook is the combination of immediate constituent and transformation grammar in Paul Roberts' *English Sentences.* Traditional grammar, whether over-simple as in the school tradition or over-complex as in the scholarly tradition, does not reveal the language as it operates.[16]

Christensen's third sentence is crucial, of course, but it is also interesting that he finds so valuable the most recently published school grammar, one which itself emphasizes a sense of structure, and a core of basic principles, presentable in an intellectually respectable way to young students.[17]

Whatever the differences in today's conceptions of grammar and rhetoric for the classroom, they are all characterized by a rigorous approach. One may clutch this fact as he moves from the comparatively simple matters of language into the complexities of literature.

T. S. Eliot says somewhere that since we probably can never be right about so great an artist as Shakespeare, perhaps it is a good thing from time to time to change our way of being wrong. Certainly the idea of what the structure of our study of literature should be shifts around; and though much period color may be merely sartorial or tonsorial, we can surely say that this is the age of analysis and one in which literary criticism is an ornament of the culture.

Literary Criticism

One very recent book, *The Modern Critical Spectrum,*[18] makes the following divisions:

[16] *Ibid.,* pp. 156–157. Reprinted with the permission of the National Council of Teachers of English.

[17] "*English Sentences* is meant for, and addressed to, high school students." Paul Roberts, *English Sentences* (New York: Harcourt, Brace & World, 1962), p. viii.

[18] Ed. Gerald J. and Nancy Marmer Goldberg (Englewood Cliffs, N.J.: Prentice-Hall, Inc., 1962).

Graham C. Wilson

1. The uses of formal analysis
2. The socio-cultural milieu
3. The uses of biography
4. The uses of tradition
5. The uses of humanism
6. The uses of scholarship
7. The uses of psychology
8. The uses of myth

This is a lot of uses and a lot of milieux. I consider all these approaches relevant to talking about our structure. The one thing they have in common is the demand for very close reading. They all assume that speed-reading does not apply to literature. This emphasis may be dated. Here are some texts that take the formalist view:

1936 *An Approach to Literature,* Cleanth Brooks, Robert Penn Warren, and John T. Purser.
1938 *Understanding Poetry,* Brooks and Warren.
1943 *Understanding Fiction,* Brooks and Warren.
1945 *Understanding Drama,* Brooks and R. B. Heilman.
1957 *Literary Criticism: A Short History,* Brooks and W. K. Wimsatt.

These volumes may be variously described, but they all emphasize close textual study, and they use a large number of closely defined terms. Three terms in the glossary of *Understanding Fiction,* for example, are *allegory, imagery, theme.* Something of what these words mean can be taught to anybody at any age. They are inherent in the conception of the structure of the study of literature today. Suppose we take *allegory.* Of it, Augusta Walker writes:

> An allegory is a kind of yarn made up to inveigle its audience into a larger idea, and the obvious difference between it and a lie is that it is always meant to lead, whereas a lie is meant to mislead. It is not a complex thing made easy, for in its fullest meaning it is no easier to understand than the original concept was. But it is more acceptable because, having meaning on several planes, it can lead its audience step by step, at least as far as they can individually go. It is never a

complication of a simple thing, which perversion would render it fraudulent.[19]

I think that this definition would embrace Aesop's fables, the parables of Jesus Christ, Nathaniel Hawthorne's *The Marble Faun* or *The House of the Seven Gables,* Thomas Mann's *The Magic Mountain,* in which ailing Europe is treated as a tuberculosis sanitorium, George Orwell's *Animal Farm* and *1984,* Alberto Moravia's *The Conformist,* Ernest Hemingway's *The Old Man and the Sea,* and Shirley Jackson's *The Lottery.*

The convention remains the same from the comparative transparency of Aesop to the opacity of Hawthorne. I cannot solve the curricular and pedagogical complications of taking the student from the deviltry of one to the diabolism of the other, but that the concept of spirality applies to the business of literary analysis I have no doubt. At some level, any student can penetrate the surface of art and this is the way you come to understand it.

Some years ago, Margaret Mead[20] addressed herself to

> . . . a specific problem: the extent to which the capacity to appreciate a literary medium and to create within it is rooted in the culture as the child experiences it in infancy and early childhood. Children become familiar with a basic imagery long before they go to school. It is in these early years that children will either learn to think in images, to endow their outer experiences with inner meaning and their inner feelings with form derived from the outer world, or will learn to live efficiently and quite contented in a world of very low symbolization, or to feel that life is unbearable because there are no symbols for what is intensely felt or that life is so overwhelmingly over-symbolized that there is no place for the imagination to work at all.

Among other things, she indicates that imagery is itself a restructuring of experience to enrich it or to make it bearable.

One of the faces of the contemporary attitude toward the

---

[19] "Allegory: A Light Conceit," *Partisan Review,* XXII, No. 4 (Fall, 1955), 483–484.

[20] Reprinted by permission of the Modern Language Association from "Cultural Bases for Understanding Literature," *Publication of the Modern Language Association,* LXVIII, No. 2 (April 1953), 12–13, 19.

structure of literature is imagery, a likeness, a mental image like something one has previously experienced or had knowledge of. We find it all over the place—a cold fish, a hot potato, "But Marie, you're so cold," said Jack frostily. We find it in literature—"that time of year thou mayst in me behold"; "the winter of our discontent"; "my life is in the sere and yellow leaf." [21] Imagery proceeds from the decorative to the organic. In some poetic drama, it may be a principal means of interpretation. *Julius Caesar* and *Coriolanus* are examples. Certainly the concept of imagery too has its spirality. It can be presented in a respectable way at almost any level to establish that it is a part of literature and not just a part of talking about literature. And finally there are a limited number of themes in literature, most of which come early within a student's understanding. But there is something else.

> . . . It has not yet been sharply enough seen that what relates American novelists to each other and so makes possible a comprehensive view of their accomplishment is not a place (e.g., regionalism) or a moment (the lost generation) or a textbook category (naturalism), but the habit of response to the impact of experience whereby they do appear to communicate within the same world of narrative discourse.[22]

This statement opens up an entire area for contemplation about structure in teaching literature. Leatherstocking is not only a character in James Fenimore Cooper; he is a mythic type, and his specific qualities endure from the Finger Lakes of New York to the African safaris of Ernest Hemingway, from *The Bride Comes to Yellow Sky* to *High Noon*. J. D. Salinger and Mark Twain have a good deal more in common than the fact that they both have written books about adolescent boys. One line of attitude and treatment in American literature comes through Henry James, and another comes through Mark Twain. Partly, of course, this is simply literary history. But

[21] L. C. Knight, "Shakespeare's Imagery," in *The Living Shakespeare,* ed. Robert Gittings (Greenwich: Fawcett Publications, 1961).
[22] R. W. B. Lewis, "Contemporary American Literature," in *Contemporary Literary Scholarship: A Critical Review,* ed. Lewis Leary, p. 212. Copyright © 1958, Appleton-Century-Crofts, Inc. Reprinted by permission of Appleton-Century-Crofts.

partly also it results from the not very surprising fact that the nature of American life and the development of American society emphasize certain elements of life and certain aspects of experience over a long period of time, from James Fenimore Cooper to Gary Cooper, as Henry Bamford Parkes has made clear in "The Metamorphoses of Leatherstocking." [23] No student should be expected to comprehend these things *ex abrupto,* but it should not be too much to hope that when he reads *The Catcher in the Rye,* he will not only feel that Holden is real and contemporary, but that he has a good many things in common with Huck Finn.

All this is simply to say that allegory, imagery, and theme are a part of literature for all ages, and thus inherent in all reading. There should be no real difficulty in talking about these matters to very young students. Mayer says that ". . . greatness in literature, by common consent, is the product of profound insight into the human condition. Adolescents are still in the process of achieving the human condition, and they cannot recognize the quality of insights into experiences they have not yet absorbed." [24]

I only half believe this. I understand from James Squire[25] that during the junior high school years many children read more extensively than during any other time in their lives and that during that period their permanent tastes for literature are more easily developed than during any other period. Contemporary scholarship and criticism are distinguished parts of our culture. One may complain that there is too much literary criticism these days, but one can hardly say that critical methods do not provide us with ways to enrich anyone's experience of literature. The structure of the junior high school student apparently indicates he is ready for more reading; the structure of our teaching should take advantage of this fact.

I doubt that an over-all structure in the discipline called English can be satisfactorily demonstrated. It remains, as some-

---

[23] "Metamorphoses of Leatherstocking," *Modern Writing No. 3,* ed. William Phillips and Philip Rahv (New York: Berkeley Publishing Company, 1956).
[24] Martin Mayer, *The Schools* (New York: Doubleday & Company, Anchor Books, 1963), p. 236.
[25] *Op. cit.,* p. 34.

one has said of history, "a sack of snakes." I have suggested here, though, that it might be useful to think of English as language and literature, and that if we do, we can discover a good deal of order. Twentieth-century study of language has given us new insights into the nature of languages and into their structures. Twentieth-century literary criticism has done the same things for literature. Twentieth-century common sense—and of course, insight—tells us much about how and when this knowledge may be best placed in the classroom. Somewhere there must be a little twentieth-century money to enable us to work out the details and to begin the job.

MICHAEL SCRIVEN

•

THE STRUCTURE OF THE
SOCIAL STUDIES

I propose to discuss this subject under the following headings:
the definition of the social sciences and the social studies; their
relationship; the effects of views about their relationship on the
curriculum; the prospects of the social sciences, and the effects
of these prospects on future curricular structures; and, finally,
the connection of values and propaganda with the social
studies.

DEFINITION OF THE SOCIAL SCIENCES AND SOCIAL STUDIES

The conventional listing of the social sciences and the social
studies can be represented as in Figure 1.

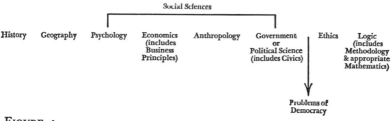

FIGURE 1

History and geography are the two with the largest share of the
curriculum at the moment. Then there are the "classical" social
sciences: psychology, sociology, anthropology, economics, and a

subject that is referred to as government or political science, depending upon one's view of it. This embraces the social sciences "proper."

The social studies, as the term is commonly used, are said to include the social sciences and also possibly the fields of ethics and logic. I use the term *"ethics"* for what is conventionally referred to as "educating citizens into acceptable standards of socio-cultural behavior." I also use the traditional term *"logic"* instead of "developing correct analytical patterns of thought."

Can we give a precise general definition of the social sciences, or of the social studies? The answer is we cannot; there is no general definition of any value. You can give a definition that is sufficiently vague to include them all, but so vague that it is useless. If you attempt to give a reasonably precise definition, it does not fit them all. For example, you might suppose that we could define the social sciences as the studies of man's social behavior. This excludes individual psychology, regional geography, and physical anthropology, which are all respectable claimants to being parts of a social science. And it includes girl watching, game theory, and gossip columns, which are all certainly studies of man's social behavior. If you add the term scientific, that is, if you say that social sciences are the scientific studies of man's social behavior, then you buy yourself a dose of circularity, which is unhelpful, and you automatically exclude history. In any satisfactory definition of science, a distinction is made between history and science. Thus, you find yourself in the dilemma of either giving a definition too general to be of any use, or a specific one that does not refer exclusively to the subject. This difficulty about definition reflects a conceptual difficulty of much more interest. It reflects the fact that the social sciences do not have the unity that people sometimes try to squeeze them into by talking in extremely vague or general terms.

RELATIONSHIP OF THE SOCIAL SCIENCES

I propose now to discuss the question of the relationship of the social sciences, and the question of the extent of their unity and diversity. There are three rough groupings of views about the relations of the social sciences. The first, which I shall call the *inter-disciplinary,* views the social sciences as specializations of a common subject matter. According to this view, one thinks of social science as a substantial subject that proliferates like the branches of a tree. A second view, which I refer to as the *multi-disciplinary* position, sees the social sciences as independent sciences concerned with aspects of human behavior which are related only by the fact that the behavior is performed by the same organism. Here the social sciences are not part of a single tree, but are a number of independently rooted trees that happen to grow in the same earth, the study of human behavior. Third, we have a far-out view that is popular among people with a strong feeling for the unity of science; this is a *reductionist* view. According to this view, the social sciences are gross preliminary studies of macrophysics. That is, since human beings are just collections of atoms, the social sciences are really just very complicated parts of physics. When the social sciences are fully developed, we shall be able to do "social sciences" by feeding the appropriate data about the constitutive atoms into a computer, which will then turn out all the conclusions that we now laboriously seek by using the conceptual terminology and theories of the social sciences themselves. Of course, the social sciences are not the only ones who would lose their individuality under this theory. Chemistry, for example, would also be eliminated; chemistry is simply macrophysics, only one level of organization up from physics. Biology is one level further up; psychology is one level further up; sociology, one level further still. This is a view, which in terms of our arboreal analogy, I will call the "forest and sawdust" view, a title that is self-explanatory, although perhaps something should be built into it about returning to ashes.

Before I say something more specific about those views, Figure 2 is a diagram which seems to me to be useful in relating the social sciences, and indeed all the subjects we have mentioned as the social studies. Such diagrams, particularly in books on philosophy of science or education, are often thought by their producers to encapsulate some great insight.

I picture the social sciences as a rectangular surface supported on a tripod. The three legs are the three subjects that have some claim to being foundational social sciences, two of which have acquired a primary place in the curriculum. The three subjects are geography, history, and one that is primary not in the secondary curriculum but in theoretical discussions of the structure of the social sciences—psychology.

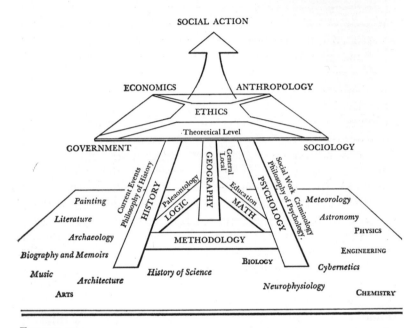

FIGURE 2

Now, why are these three primary? This is the reason; geography is the study of the spatial distribution of man and his large-scale effects on the earth. History is the study of his temporal distribution and achievements, and psychology is the study of the internal organization of the human entity.

On these three legs rest the social sciences as they are commonly conceived. But, these legs will not hold together, they could not support anything were it not for the general application of methodology, the laws of logic, and mathematics (in particular, statistics). The methodology is that which enables you to get somewhere from the basic observations; the logic enables you to sustain consistency and examine analytically:

the mathematics enables you to squeeze intelligible laws out of the complex data of the social sciences.

The general surface on which this whole structure rests, for indeed the social sciences are dependent upon other subjects, is the surface of the physical and biological sciences. Nothing that is a statement in psychology could be true were it not that certain physical and biological statements are also true. Learning would not be possible unless there was relative stability in the molecules that make up the oxygen processing system of the human organism, and so on. So there is something that underlies the social sciences: it is the physical and biological sciences.

Geography forms one strut of the tripod, psychology one, and history one. When I talk about geography, I think not only of the rudimentary, factual material which is an important, indispensable part of the subject, but also of the more abstract discussions of the nature of geography in Hartshorne and others. I'm going to call that the philosophy of geography. Similarly with history and with psychology, as one moves from the basic data through current applications, one moves toward the higher level of abstractions—the theoretical and philosophical—where questions about the nature of the subject arise.

Those of you who have not made a special study of geography in the past few years may be unaware of the extent to which the philosophy of geography is a hotly debated, exciting, and indeed very informative subject. It is informative, among other reasons, because it provides us with a model of the social sciences which is quite unlike that of classical physics. The latter comparison is likely to lead to far more harm than good, and has in fact done so, a point to which we will return in a moment.

On the tripod rests the surface that represents the standard social sciences of the academic curriculum: sociology, government, economics, and anthropology. They depend in varying ways on geography, history, and psychology, and I've tried to represent their varying degrees of dependency by their position. Sociology, for example, is loosely connected with psychology. Government includes civics and political science. Economics includes business. Business, properly taught, stands in exactly the same relationship to economics that comparative government stands to political science. If it's academically respectable to teach comparative institutions in a government course, then it's academically respectable to teach a large part of the material that goes into a *good* business course.

Now, these subjects all merge; no subject in the entire social studies curriculum is devoid of contamination by each other subject. For example, every one of these subjects, when taught in any conceivably defensible way, involves some reference to historical examples. Typically, it involves some reference to geographical examples. Typically, it involves some dependence upon psychological laws, or generalizations. Anthropology itself is closely connected to sociology, government, and so on. So, these are distinctions, not between subjects that are rigidly separated, but between subjects that merge.

Running through each of these subjects is a particular ethical thread. For example, in economics, the sub-subject called welfare economics is concerned with the application of, or the analysis of, the consequences of value judgments of various kinds, through economic theory. The attempt to apply economics to any actual situation (changing the tariff, redistributing the income system) involves welfare economics because it involves value judgments. A great part of anthropology is concerned with moral behavior as it is conceived in various societies. In government we have political philosophy, which of course embodies value judgments without end; the Platonic theory of the state commits itself to a certain kind of value set, and the democratic theory commits itself to a different kind, and so on. In sociology the sub-field is not precisely defined in a standard way at the moment, but I shall call it moral dynamics. There has been a good deal of discussion of the operation of explicit and implicit mores in a society, the kind of pressures exerted in a particular culture, and the way in which they work.

In the center of all this, at the pivot point of the whole system, is the subject of ethics itself. The reason for this location is a very simple one; this is the point of support for any practical action: action in general rests on this surface and has to be supported by it, if it is to be defensible at all. So behavior, or action, or plans of various kinds, since they involve other people (thinking now of behavior in the social area), automatically involve ethics.

THE SOCIAL STUDIES CURRICULUM

What follows from the various views of the relationship and unity of the social sciences? I think that my schema suggests something about the relative ordering of the sciences, something that is somewhat lost in other accounts. In a real sense, certain of the social sciences *are* prior to the others in that they must be laid down, or set up, before the others can be laid down. You can't teach these latter subjects adequately without some reference to psychological, historical, and geographical material. And in so far as it is possible to defend the emphasis on these three subjects in the current social studies curriculum, this seems to me to be the way to do it. In addition there is another argument for the priority of psychology, history, and geography, not in epistemological terms but in pedagogical terms, viz, that this part of the social studies curriculum is considerably simpler to teach.

However, one might ask, "What about psychology? How can one teach this at the elementary level?" I think the answer to that question is that one can, and very easily. Lippitt, for example, has been teaching some quite sophisticated aspects of group dynamics at the second- and third-grade level, without noticeable difficulty, by extremely ingenious teaching methods. These methods involve role acting, in which a particular teacher-child relationship is set up by a small group which rehearses it extensively and acts it out in front of the class. They take a very defensive teacher, to begin with, or a very aggressive child, and attempt first to explain this behavior, and then to make suggestions to improve harmony. These suggestions are applied in a new play-acting, and the class then comments on the extent to which this bears out, or counts against, the theory they had before, and so on. This is not only very exciting for the children, but also very fruitful, for they come up with generalizations which, in my view, are as serious as those to be found in most of the classical works on the subject of small-group behavior. And their generalizations are much more intelligent in the sense that they are less "highfalutin" and much nearer to common sense.

I think, however, that there are also epistemological reasons for supposing that these subjects are prior to the others, and Figure 2 incorporates that priority. Even though that priority exists, it is not absolutely binding. It is not inconceivable that one could begin the social studies curriculum with anthropology; it's not inconceivable that you could begin with economics—because it's being done.

What would be the advantages and disadvantages of these approaches? I think that all one can say here is that the curricula organized in these different ways must speak for themselves, and we must look at their results to determine their value.

I hope we shall see more experimentation along these lines. I am only giving a plausible defense of one ordering. One important position that is incorporated in this picture is the view that the whole *inter*-disciplinary approach, as it is often conceived, is mistaken. There is no common subject that branches out into various other subjects. The whole structure of the social sciences is the structure of these sciences and their linkage. They are not branches from some common core. The attempts to produce that common core always result in absurdly vague and worthless generalizations about human behavior. It is much more valuable to begin by giving students something substantial under these various headings, and later feeding them the relationships of the various subjects.

That leads us to the *multi*-disciplinary approach. This seems to me to be a much more interesting idea. If one wants to teach the social sciences, or the social studies, it seems to me that one can very usefully do so by the case-history method, by taking a particular problem—for example, the problem of poverty, or of integration, or of labor management, or of education for voting, or of the urbanization of family life, or of industrialization, many of which problems should be but are not included in Problems of Democracy courses—and then treating it in the different ways that professional scientists from each of these various studies would. Don't attempt to give the whole treatment as a homogenized hodgepodge; nothing valuable comes out of that; in fact, it's a bore, even to the people who know about the subject. It is just a forced exercise.

There are a number of different social science approaches. If you look at a problem from the point of view of the economist, you will see it in certain terms, you will see it through his glasses. That can be illuminating. See the course of history in terms of the economic motive and you generate an entire theory of an exciting kind, which could hardly be said to be without practical effects. See it through the eye of the sociologist and you see it in a different way. Now, each of these particular views of the problem is valuable, provided that its independence is preserved. The minute that you merge them, you get a smudge from which very little emerges. Also, you lose something that is extremely important—and that is, that if you were to develop the distinct viewpoints further in a particular direction you might get further research insights.

Of course, one of the most important things to remember, when you look at this vast structure of knowledge and think to yourself of the limited number of periods you have in which to get across the wealth of material in these subjects, is the necessity of stimulating interest in further learning. You might say that the only way to teach the social studies is to make the child learn them by himself because it's too much for you to teach. But if you're going to do that, don't try to do it by pouring everything into a bowl, blending it briskly, and then feeding them the resulting pablum. Try to give them a meal that will have interest because of its independent elements.

The *reductionist* is a man of very different caliber. His argument is that the social sciences are a sort of excrescence on the surface of the physical and biological sciences, and indeed the biological sciences are a superficial film on the physical sciences, all of which will be done away with in the fullness of time with the further development of atomic physics. Now this is unrealistic, obviously, but it might still be true.

Is it true? I think not, and I think there are a great many compelling reasons *why* not. The most important reason for the separate existence, and the *eternal* separate existence, of physics and the social sciences, is that their tasks are quite different. The task of the social sciences is to operate with the data that are accessible about the entity under scrutiny at a certain point in its life-history. If we could get all the data we wanted, then we might be able to do the whole thing with physics. But we can't. The problem is that the child comes in and says, "My parents want me to be a doctor; I don't like the idea, I would much rather be an automobile mechanic. What should I do?" And we are now too late in the game to be able to go back and dig up the interaction between the molecules in his body and the cosmic rays from outer space which no doubt altered his activity at some early stage. We are not even in a position to get hold of the structure of his genes, and the late-maturing ones in there will of course have some effect on his subsequent capacity in these various directions. We are not even in a position to know what we would need to know about much of the later physical development of this organism—in order to get the data for that, we would have to perform a post-mortem. And this would rather defeat the object of the enterprise.

We should think of the social sciences as sciences whose task is to work from a certain body of available data to the solution of certain problems of great importance. If no holds were barred, the reductionist might be right. But a lot of holds are barred; we are not allowed to kill the subjects to find out what's in their brains; we are not even allowed to perform controlled experiments that might involve severe punishments, or sustain deprivation of love of the control group, and so on. So the social sciences are, in this sense, games with incomplete rules—sciences of incomplete data. There will never be a complete body of data. So, the reductionist is not going to be a serious threat to us, a fact that is obvious commonsensically, but not quite so obvious philosophically.

PROSPECTS

I want to turn now to my final topics—the prospects of the social sciences and the effects of views about this and their structure on curriculum; and finally the values and propaganda problem.

A great deal of the difficulty in getting the social sciences into the social studies curriculum in an academically respectable form arises from the lack of agreement amongst social scientists as to the nature of their subjects. A great part of this disagreement, and the consequent confusion, springs from the use of an inappropriate model for the social sciences. There are many aspects of this problem. I propose here to comment briefly on the relationship between the social sciences and the physical sciences.

We have already discussed that relationship in one way, i.e., the dispensability of the social sciences. But there is another way in which the physical sciences affect the social sciences, and this is in terms of their role as a model, an ideal. There are very few social scientists who do not believe that the physical sciences are in some sense a paradigm for science. There are some exceptions, but typically a sociologist is likely to agree that he would like to see sociology develop in the direction of becoming more like field theory in physics, with its greater precision, its greater powers of prediction, its more complicated theories, and its more exciting theories. The same applies to the psychologist. Indeed, there has been a long history of psychologists who have attempted to produce theories of learning, for example, which are patterned upon classical physical theories. In my view, all of this is now a waste of time and a seriously misleading way of looking at the social sciences. If I had to produce a model subject for the social sciences which would attract me strongly, I think that geography would be the one. Geography is a really messy subject. There are a lot of facts; for example, New York is on the eastern coast of the United States. But when we get beyond the level of facts and try to produce a generalization that is any good in geography, we run into difficulties. We can produce generalizations, e.g., about the climate in California, which aren't bad, but somehow these have a sort of parochial look; they are not like the universal law of gravitation. Somehow, one feels it would be better, the subject would be more scientific, if we could precisely deduce this sort of local law from some kind of all-enveloping law or theory of the kind found in physics.

The point that I want to support about the social sciences is that the attempt to pattern them after the physical sciences is a mistake. The task of the social sciences, and its ultimate task, is to produce low-level generalizations of some value and explain them in a rather informal way. There will never be vast theories that embrace the whole of the social sciences. People often talk about the day when the Newton of the social sciences will arrive and will produce a systematic theory that will do for social sciences what Newton did for astronomy and physics. There will be no such day. Now, these are very strong claims. But I think that the grounds for saying this are overwhelming; and we are misled to the contrary by an extremely naive picture of science.

Further illustration of this point is the contrast between the social sciences and astronomy. The basic fact about astronomy is that it is ludicrously simple. The main difficulty was converting astronomical observations into orbital position. Finding out what motions the stars and planets actually have from what we see in the sky is tricky. But, as a matter of fact, once they are mapped, the whole thing becomes a rather elementary exercise. That is, the paths, the orbits, are almost perfect elementary geometrical loci. And what a stroke of fortune! The law that explains this is an inverse square law with three variables, two of them of the same kind. Almost ludicrously simple—it doesn't *quite* work (the Einsteinian corrections have to be taken into account) but it very nearly works for very nearly everything in sight. The law of falling bodies on the earth's surface, air resistance apart, is fantastically simple. The thing to remember about early physicists and astronomers is that they were just lucky, they struck pure gold.

Now, the social sciences are not young sciences which may some day arrive at the stage of astronomy—they are the oldest of all the sciences. There's nothing young about psychology. If you decide to limit the use of the term "psychology," or the term "scientific psychology," to what has happened since the time of Wundt, then you are perfectly entitled to do so, but the fact remains that the objective, rational study of (and theorizing about) human behavior was going strong two thousand years before that—Aristotle's psychology is not to be dismissed. It could certainly be defended as saying more illuminating things about human behavior in general than S-R theory does. It does not say precise and exact things about limited areas in special learning situations; that is a valuable contribution of recent psychology. But to call that the beginning of psychology is absurd. It's like arguing that the physical sciences include only those observations made under microscopes. They do not; they include observations on the large scale as well. Observations on the very large scale in the physical sciences such as astronomy led to fairly simple results. In the social sciences, they did not. But might this not be only the present situation?

There are at least thirty crucial variables in the problem of predicting how well a student will do in college on the basis of what you can know about him in the twelfth grade. In predicting the behavior of a planet, on the basis of what you know about it five years before you want to predict it, there is only one, or perhaps two or three variables, depending on the way you do it. The social sciences are just tougher. That's why it's harder to produce generalizations in the social sciences, and that's why they will always be at a lower level. By the nature of the case, there are too many unpredictable, interfering variables of crucial importance in the social sciences. And they will never be eliminated. The idea that there might one day arise a Newton of the social sciences is like the idea that one day we will all be robots coming out of a relatively simple factory. Well, we may be; and if *that* happens, the Newton of the social sciences will be able to come along and produce general laws of human behavior. But as long as we are the people that we are today, as complicated as we are today, there won't be a Newton because his task would be demonstrably impossible.

You might think this is a little tough on Sigmund Freud, who in a certain sense did produce some underlying generalizations of a relatively exciting kind. I would want to argue about various aspects of this, but at no point would I want to say that his suggestions were less than brilliant; nor would I want to say that they didn't contain some truth. I would want to add that after fifty years we still don't know just how much truth they do contain—which seems to me rather unfortunate. Even if you take them in the form in which they have been reasonably substantiated, they tell you nothing, or almost nothing, about how certain children in a classroom with a particular teacher are going to behave. They tell you nothing about what will happen if the President says he will immediately go to war if anybody sets a foot in West Berlin. Freudian theory, while it's often thought to be very general, and it is in several respects fairly general, has nothing in any way comparable to the kind of generality that the Newtonian laws have.

Of course these are controversial remarks, and they're intended to stimulate thinking rather than to serve as proofs of the conclusions I'm offering. I do want you to think about the possibility that the social sciences should be conceived, not as ineffectual, bumbling, weak sisters of the physical sciences, but as subjects of which I would say the following: In the twentieth century, *the* major contribution to the history of science has been the development of scientific method in psychology and sociology. In the same period, discoveries have been made in physics of very great importance—relativity theory was a very great discovery. But none represented something wholly new in the conception of scientific method. The introduction of the highly controlled experimental designs involving many variables, the analysis of variance, the development of t tests, descriptive statistics, the analysis of covariance, and other tools have now made it possible to extract interesting relationships of a causal and correlational kind from data that were previously useless. The domain of rational inquiry has been extended in the social sciences in the twentieth century in a way quite unlike the way in which advances have been made in physics. Physicists have developed new tools and new theories, but not new methods in the sense that I am talking about. The great step forward in the social sciences has been their development to a level where they can produce quantified accounts of phenomena, although not quantitative theories, and extract from data that were previously useless, material of great value.

In my view, statistics and Fisherian experimental design are the great instruments of scientific method in the twentieth century. We have no need, as social scientists or people very interested in the social sciences, to hang our heads in any way if we are compared with physical scientists. To me there is great excitement in seeing a way to go about designing an experiment that may answer an incredibly difficult and complex problem in the social sciences. This is not feeble groping in the dark, or doing something that is preliminary to the great moment in the social sciences. The great moment has already come! The question is, how much work do we do?

SOCIAL STUDIES AND CITIZENSHIP EDUCATION

Some marvelous statements are made about the social studies and moral behavior: "All education, we may assume, is aimed at the transmission of the values of our culture, and the development of socially acceptable attitudes towards problems and conflicts." That's the opening sentence of a paper by Preston James, an academician, in the volume that the American Council of Learned Societies and the National Council for the Social Studies produced on the social sciences and social studies.[1] The same volume contains a postscript in which the following sentence occurs: "An education is expected to take all the youth, and by means of twelve or more years of schooling, to secure their dedication to the values of the democratic society. . . ."[2] The National Council for the Social Studies itself is on record as saying that the ultimate goal of education in the social studies is the "development of desirable socio-civic behavior."

Rubbish! Not only rubbish, but "socio-civically" repulsive. *If* we are concerned with ethics, as those authors assert, then a basic theorem in ethics asserts the right of the individual to make up his own mind on fundamental issues of conduct. That gives us as teachers only the right, indeed in our society the duty, of placing in front of the individual certain facts about the alternatives that are open to him politically and socially, and teaching him the skills that are necessary to assess those facts. It does not give us the right, let alone the duty, to stuff our solution down his throat or in any way to force it on him, except in so far as the facts themselves sell it to him. The remarks quoted are objectionable because in the name of morality they advocate immoral behavior.

How is one who is already committed to a certain way of life going to refrain from getting some of it across? He is not. It's fine if he does. Students *should* be taught by persons with

[1] ACLS/NCSS, *The Social Studies and the Social Sciences* (New York: Harcourt, Brace & World, 1962), p. 42.
[2] *Ibid.*, p. 289.

enthusiasm for their particular solutions to problems. But it is not impossible for a man to have great enthusiasm for his solution to a problem and yet to represent the other side fairly; nor is it impossible to have supporters of different views present their points of view with equal enthusiasm to the student.

This is certainly not a novel position, yet it ought to be something on which the citizens of a democracy take a very strong stand. What is it that we think to be the crucial difference between the school system in our country and that in totalitarian countries? It is that in those countries propaganda is put across in the classroom. The remarks quoted earlier are explicit encouragement to propaganda, as opposed to explicit commitment to learning. Education is not "aimed at the transmission of the values of our culture." It is aimed at the transmission of the facts about our culture and other cultures, and the skills that are needed to make the choices a responsible citizen must make. It is also aimed at getting across the facts about what happens if you mix sodium chloride with all sorts of other dull things, which has nothing to do with the transmission of our values. It is dedicated to a great many things; but to say that the purpose of education is to convert children to our way of thinking is to say that the purpose of education is to deny them the right of choice. It is to say that we must abandon the principles of democracy in order to instill them.

Well, enough of that particular anti-slogan sloganing; I'm only anxious that you see the importance of that particular side of the debate about what the social studies are supposed to do. Selling the principles of democracy and socially acceptable behavior by giving good reasons for them is an admirable undertaking, provided that you also give good reasons, the best reasons, for the alternatives. Selling them by brainwashing is to sell them out.

ETHICS

Finally I want to say something about the ethics situation, as one might put it. We might as well finish with a slightly controversial position for a change, and I'll say this: The strength of religion in this society has led us to adopt a curious kind of cultural myth. It is the myth that ethics is somehow dependent upon religion.

The fact of the matter, as virtually every theologian will tell you, is that it's impossible to found a moral system upon a set of theological beliefs. Any good theologian of any persuasion, Catholic or Protestant or otherwise, will immediately be very upset by the suggestion that the basis for Christian morality is fear of hell; behavior prompted by such fear would not be moral behavior. The message of Christian morality is that you act morally from love of our Savior. Or as the humanists point out, it is more economical and less metaphysical to do it from love of your fellow man *directly,* not because you love some other entity who wants you to love your fellows, since what you're going to have to do ultimately is love the other person.

I don't like to give treatments of the whole of ethics in a short statement, but I would like to indicate that it is my view at the moment that there is no logical respect in which ethics is different from any other part of the social studies, except that it is often more complicated, and it finishes up with propositions about moral behavior instead of economic behavior. There is nothing special about terms like "good," "best," "ought," and "should"; they are not specifically moral terms; they occur in every field of practical activity and in all the social sciences.

If you ask me which is the *best* dishwasher now available, regardless of price, I can tell you. Now that doesn't involve moral judgment, but it does involve a value judgment. And I get that value judgment by considering the various dimensions along which one rationally evaluates dishwashers, i.e., those that are demonstrably relevant to its task, and then seeing which of the ones I am comparing scores best on these dimensions. There is no difference in principle between that and the evaluation of alternative courses of behavior. The experiment at Harvard, in which students are being trained to give ethical analyses of problem situations without commitment to a special set of values (they analyze problems in terms of alternative possible sets of values), has demonstrated something which Professor

Michael Scriven

Frankena has often said: There are almost no debates in the ethical field which are not debates about facts. The way he puts it is that he has never had a moral argument with anybody which ended at a point where one of them could only say, "Well, this is my ultimate value, and I haven't any way to support it." People will always go on and say their view is right, because "What would it be like if everybody behaved in your way?" Well, that is a question the social scientist can answer, or if he can't answer it, he knows how to go about answering it. And if he can't solve it at the moment, he solves it in terms of uncertainties. So moral solutions are still possible, since there is a moral solution appropriate for conditions of ignorance about outcomes just as another will be appropriate if the outcome is known to be of a certain kind.

SUMMARY

Let me sum up what I have been saying in this way. The social sciences have a certain relationship to each other, and to ethics, and to logic, and to the other sciences. I have endeavored to indicate one way in which this can be pictured. It follows from this account of their relationship, if it's a sound account, that certain conceptions of the possibility of interdisciplinary approaches to the social science curriculum are likely to be unfortunate. It also follows that the idea of the social sciences as wholly independent is likely to be misleading. And for other reasons, which I mentioned, it is unlikely that the dispensability of the social sciences in favor of physics is either practically or epistemologically defensible. Certain general considerations about the nature of the social sciences lead one to suppose that their future is not going to follow the path of astronomy, and that it would be well to recognize this explicitly at this stage. For reasons that are already clear, the nature of these subjects is essentially quite restricted by their complexity, and it is in finding comprehensible theories at this level of complexity that their future and value lie.

Finally, I said something about the relationship of the social studies to teaching behavior to future citizens. I made two main claims. If it is the task of the social studies curriculum to discuss moral problems, and I believe that it is, and if the moral values that are supposed to be encouraged are those of democracy, then it cannot be the task of the social studies to sell those values in the way in which it is often thought they should be sold, that is, by inculcating them, by transmitting them by force of prestige or authority, because the basic values of democracy are incompatible with that kind of procedure. Second, in discussing the ethics aspect of the social studies curriculum, I said that it seems to be very important to emphasize that there is no way in which ethics depends upon religion, and there is no way in which ethics is any different from any other applied subject. Ethics, with the help of the social sciences, concerns questions like, "What shall I do if I want to help this state to prosper in the next ten years?" "What shall I do if I want criminals to become better citizens?" The value behind answers to such questions is the very simple value that people have equal rights; and if you want to argue about that, then we can give straightforward, though long-winded, utilitarian justifications of it. While if you're prepared to go so far with democracy as to accept the principle of equal rights, then you automatically have the basis for the whole of ethics. In short, you might as well face the fact that if we're going to start talking about social action and hence ethics, at all, its place is right in the center of the social studies.

PRINTED IN U.S.A.